The
Diary of an
Angry
Commuter

Sara
Yirrell

Matador
9 Priory Business Park,
Wistow Road, Kibworth Beauchamp,
Leicestershire. LE8 0RX
Tel: (+44) 116 279 2299
Fax: (+44) 116 279 2277
Email: books@troubador.co.uk
Web: www.troubador.co.uk/matador

ISBN 978 1788039 505

British Library Cataloguing in Publication Data.
A catalogue record for this book is available from the British Library.

Printed and bound in the UK by 4edge limited
Typeset in 11pt Minion Pro by Troubador Publishing Ltd, Leicester, UK

Matador is an imprint of Troubador Publishing Ltd

I'd like to dedicate this to all those who encouraged me to turn my regular online rants into a book; particularly my mum, Rosa.

Author Foreword

Commuting by rail is a whole different world, and it makes normally sane, rational people lose all sense of perspective.

Anyone just starting out in their commuting life (you poor thing) needs to be aware that there is train etiquette to follow, and woe betide you if you fail to follow the rules.

Failure to adhere to these rules (which change on a regular basis) means your cards will be marked.

The various travelling cliques – whether it is the trendy media types that share a table every evening, or the bunch of Friday drinkers that like to block vestibule areas or passageways as they celebrate the end of another week, the bunch of lawyers and posh gits on the verge of retirement who always catch up in the evenings when the train is pulling into your station – will remember your face and you will be made to suffer in some way.

Commuters are not shy in expressing their displeasure at someone sitting in 'their' seat, or encroaching in their space, but they will band together over the unlikeliest of things. Their behaviour cannot be predicted.

When you are actually a commuter, the things you witness will shock, annoy, enrage and amuse you in equal measure.

Believe it or not, some commuters even take petty pleasure in other people losing their tickets, being made to move seats, arguing with the guard, and missing the train altogether. They may not show it, but they do, because it means they are not suffering alone.

It serves those casual travellers right for not taking out a second mortgage just to get to work each day, they think.

As a commuter, you have low-to-zero tolerance for anything transpiring on that miserable, cramped and dirty train you are forced onto most days.

You swear under your breath far more times than you care to mention. You sometimes forget the manners you were taught by your parents. Although some people on trains clearly were not taught any manners to start with.

You are constantly aware of the amount of money you are spending each month on your obscenely-priced season ticket.

It makes you want to cry. And while a five-minute delay on the way to London can just about be sucked up, any delay in the evening is beyond unacceptable. This is YOUR time they are stealing. The bastards.

This book was born from the many commuting experiences I had over the years, but also from the stories friends and family told me. Thanks to them for sharing!

The comments in this book, particularly the ones about children 'daring to travel' on trains, are ones I overheard from the mutterings of very grumpy regulars who clearly had had a bad day. Or were facing a bad day ahead.

Everything in this book is also written firmly tongue-in-cheek; if you are easily offended, perhaps you should cease reading now.

For non-commuters reading this, rest assured, this is exactly how anyone you know who commutes regularly will be feeling, and remember it could affect their life permanently and take years to recover from.

Having been a seasoned commuter for 17 years, I hope one day that my blood pressure will return to normal and that I won't hyperventilate when I see a train approaching.

JANUARY

Wednesday 4 January

My first day back on the railway after two whole weeks of train-free bliss over Christmas. I dragged my feet the whole way to the platform, hoping against hope that there would be some delay that I could escalate into something else and use as an excuse to work from home. For once, the train was on time. Thanks, Network Rail. The one time I long to hear 'over-running engineering works' and you actually complete on time? Damn you.

Thursday 5 January

Too tired after yesterday's trip to go into the office today. I forgot how much commuting takes it out of you. Took advantage of our company's flexible working policy today – just one day after a two-week break!

Bothered? Nope. Half of my colleagues are still on holiday anyway.

Friday 6 January

The trains are amazingly quiet today. I got two whole seats to myself for the entire journey and the trains were on time. I arrived in London with a Mona Lisa-style smile on my face. The journey home was the same. I know that the apocalypse is coming next week and I will be punished for this smugness.

Monday 9 January

Punished I was. The bloody platform was eight-deep in sodding people this morning. Where the hell have they all come from?

Where were they last week when the rest of us were suffering? The noticeboard says previous train cancelled and this one expected fifteen minutes late. FFS. Chorus of tuts as I try to make my way down the platform.

The train arrives and it is five carriages instead of eight. FIVE FUCKING CARRIAGES? Everyone pushes on, but when it's my turn there is just no room, and an old git in an overcoat decides to block the door and half smiles at me as the door closes. The train pulls off and I make a 'wanker' gesture from the platform as it departs. Working from home again today, then.

Tuesday 10 January

It is raining, but fairly mild. So of course, the trains are like Dante's inferno inside with the heaters going full blast. The moisture from people's clothing has turned the carriages into saunas. Not a single one has a normal temperature.

"Can't you turn the heat down?" I gasp at the train manager. "Sorry love," he replies. "The switch is on the outside of the train and it can't change until it is in the sidings."

WHO THE FUCK designed trains whose temperature cannot be controlled from within? Utter idiots.

Got the same train back in the evening (I know because of a mark on the table of my seat), and the temperature had actually risen. People were shiny faced and sweating by the time we got back. A few had changed into bikinis and Speedos, and there was a distinct whiff of B.O. in the air.

Wednesday 11 January

Luckily for me, a heating system problem at work means I have to work from home today. Result.

Thursday 12 January and Friday 13 January

Days off – holiday owing. Yes.

Monday 16 January

I overslept and missed my usual train by two minutes. I'm consigned to the 'New Delhi'-style express half an hour later. Instead of an hour and five minutes, this one takes an hour and forty-five minutes. It stops in the middle of nowhere for no reason, is absolutely packed out and for some reason just smells musty and slightly cheesy.

The phone reception is so shit that I spent most of the journey trying to alert my workmates that I might be a bit tardy this morning. They got the texts as I arrived, red-faced, in the office.

Tuesday 17 January

It's always a pleasure when first class is at the front of the inbound train. It usually means I don't have to share a seat. But today, two carriages were filled with schoolchildren. WHY are they allowed on commuter trains?

Don't they know we have to get to work and need some peace and quiet? Do they know how important we businesspeople actually are?

I had to sit next to someone for the whole journey to London. Ugh. But I did take some pleasure asking in a sweet voice "Is this seat free?" and making them move their great big bag, coat and laptop out the way first.

The guy in front had an empty seat next to him, but principle is everything.

Wednesday 18 January

The woman next to me today on the way home from London was sleeping with her mouth wide open, emitting the loudest snores I have ever heard.

Each one must have broken the sound barrier. I did the coughing, the sneezing and even the gentle nudging with the elbows to try to rouse her from her unattractive slumber. But nothing did. Someone was waking up in the sidings this evening.

Thursday 19 January

Drivers' strike today and tomorrow so the train service is seriously reduced. The drivers are worried about passenger safety due to some cuts coming their way and are striking in protest. My arse is it anything to do with passenger safety. Greedy bastards. Sack the lot and employ someone who wants to work.

No option to work from home today, so I cram onto the train and am standing by the rankest smelling toilet you have ever smelled. Like something crawled in there, died and crawled back out again. Probably a seasoned commuter.

The journey home was equally hellish, but managed to push an old lady out the way to claim a seat. Result.

Friday 20 January

Guard strike again. Cattle-class journey, but this time I'm sitting in a luggage rack. Anyone who asks me to move so they can put their case there will be told exactly where to go and what they can do with their stupid wheeled luggage. Someone with a small case took one look at my face and backed the fuck off.

Monday 23 January

It's Blue Monday today apparently. The most depressing day of the year when reality sets in about how we are wasting our lives with pointless work, and are extremely poor to boot because we have not yet been paid. The train was late for absolutely no reason, which put everyone in a fantastic mood.

To cheer commuters up, some happy-looking people from the train company were handing out cupcakes with blue icing in London this morning. It didn't work. Most stalked past with hate in their eyes, and the ones who took the sweet treats took one bite and deposited them in the nearest bin.

This was a rare moment when I actually felt sorry for the train people. But the moment passed very briefly when I reminded myself how much my season ticket cost.

Tuesday 24 January

A Tube strike in London today meant the trains were blissfully empty. Because I cycle to the office, the Tube strike means nothing to me! *smug grin*

Wednesday 25 January

I worked from home today. I had a lie-in and relished the thought of all my fellow commuters having to get on a train and endure the misery without me.

Thursday 26 January

I was punished for laughing at my fellow travellers yesterday. Will I ever learn? No sodding trains home due to some sort of power outage. Have these train companies not heard of bloody diesel? No information and the handful of staff on the platform had formed a defence ring with shields; nothing was penetrating their armour.

I fought my way through crowds to another station, pushed my way onto a train heading north, recognised some people from my train line, made a bee-line for them, and three and a half hours later (and significantly lighter in the pocket) we fell out of a shared taxi back in our home town.

Compensation claim number one of the year going in!

Friday 27 January

There is absolutely no way I'm going in to the office today after yesterday. I'm still traumatised over the number of hours of my life I will not get back.

Monday 30 January

The trains are still 'in the wrong place' after last week so there are heavy delays and reduced services. WTF? Ticket kiosk man just stares me out, almost daring me to argue. So I turn around and go home. How can they still be in the wrong place after four days? They just go up and down tracks don't they? Or am I missing something?

Tuesday 31 January

A guy waiting for the train this morning emits a loud, long (and pretty impressive) fart on the platform and pretends it is nothing to do with him. It was obviously louder than he anticipated as he looked quite shocked and that tell-tale redness crept into his cheeks. I can't stop laughing, but am relieved I'm not downwind. I made sure I was in a different carriage to him just in case it is a recurring problem.

I see same guy on my way home, but don't dare to look him in the eye. He looks deflated enough.

FEBRUARY

Wednesday 1 February

Standing on the platform on yet another foggy, dreary morning, I ask myself for the millionth time, *"Why the fuck am I doing this?"* I look around at the miserable, depressed faces of everyone around me and I know they are thinking the same thing.

But hey, it is lighter for a few minutes longer each day, so summer is coming, right? Nope, that makes zero difference. I hate my life. I hate commuting. And I hate people.

Thursday 2 February

I get embroiled in a door-opening stand-off this morning. I reach for the handle, just as the person inside reaches out the window to grab the handle, resulting in an awkward clash of hands. Yes, we still have some slam-door 'HST' trains on our line (as well as the more up-to-date automatic door models), but we all prefer the older trains because they are more comfortable. It is a shame the service isn't as good as it was 40 years ago too.

We both pull back in horror at the unwanted physical contact with another human being and then wait for the other to make their move. We are shocked out of our frozen state by someone hissing "For fuck's sake open the fucking door one of you". This has all happened in the space of ten seconds, but it feels like a lifetime.

My lightening reflexes mean I get there first, yank open the door and the other bloke rushes out and down the platform without making eye contact.

Friday 3 February

That heart-sinking moment when a larger-than-life person shunts themselves down the carriage and points their sausage-like fingers at the empty seat next to you. There is no way in hell they are going to fit in that seat comfortably. Particularly as we are on one of the 'newer' InterCity-style trains.

Very few people bigger than a ten-year-old actually do fit comfortably in those seats, particularly if you actually need to use your arms, or God forbid, share an armrest. I'd love to know who designed them, and let them know what I think of their designs.

I think I've put my back out leaning into the aisle during my hour-long journey, trying not to make bodily contact. Of course, there are no spare seats anywhere else on the sodding train and even the luggage racks are full.

I get off the train stuck at a 90-degree angle and catch the smug smirk on the face of the space Hoover as they lift up the dividing armrest and spread out quite literally.

Monday 6 February

To the guy who likes to run to the station every morning in full running garb. First off, you look like a dick. Second, if you ever splash me with your bodily fluids as you breeze past my seat again, I will strangle you with your ridiculous neon sweat-band. You arse.

Tuesday 7 February

I laughed out loud as a bloke came crashing down my carriage this evening and started banging frantically on the door as the train pulls away from his stop. His language was pretty colourful, which made me laugh even more, and what made it worse was he did that trippy thing where you keep running even though your legs are nearly bent double with the effort of standing up.

He stayed upright, so credit to him, but I think he managed to deal some poor woman a glancing blow off the side of her head with one flailing elbow. She wasn't happy and called him a fucking arsehole.

I managed to snort loudly as he did the walk of shame back to his seat, and earned a glare that would make birds drop out of the sky in fear.

In typical commuter fashion, I walked through to the next carriage when it was my turn to get off at the next stop, just so I didn't have to see him again.

Wednesday 8 February

Every morning I thank God for the quiet coach on my train. The one with signs that say "Please show consideration to other passengers by not listening to loud music, or making unnecessary noise."

So when some fucker gets on with shitty old iPhone headphones, and you spend the next hour listening to tinny renditions of 'Klub Klassix 1998', it is little wonder that you feel like ripping them out their ears and shoving them where the sun don't shine.

Thursday 9 February

A blissful day working from home. Oh the luxury.

Friday 10 February

Dear idiotic day tripper/tourist. When you don't use trains that often, and we happen to be on a slam-door train, and you have zero idea how the doors actually work, don't wait by the fucking door when the train pulls into the station and stand there staring at the bloody thing as if willing it to move. GET OUT OF THE SODDING WAY and let one of us do it.

Unlike you and your swanning about, we have been stuck in a shitty office all day and want to get home. These people make me want to scream.

Monday 13 February

Coming home this evening, we all played

platform bingo – much to the amusement of the staff. As ever, the regulars stand at the normal platform that the train leaves from 99.9% of the time. And with five minutes to go until leaving time (and no sign of a fricking train), we are told it is, in fact, a different platform.

By now, people are hyperventilating at the thought of someone else getting their seat, and a mad scramble ensues to get near the front of the queue. More people have now joined the platform party.

Some are hovering between platforms just in case. I sometimes do that, but it never works in my favour.

This time, the hoverers are the winners, as the train pulls into the original platform, and ignoring all the passengers trying to get off, a massive crowd of desperate, besuited individuals start running towards the train at top speed. It is chaos. Blood is usually shed somewhere along the line.

Tuesday 14 February

The sight of loads of men coming home late from work clutching the most pathetic bunch of withered flowers never ceases to amuse me on Valentine's Day. Of course, you get a few smug bastards (probably newly-weds) who are carrying monster bouquets of expensive, fragrant flowers, and you can physically feel the hate directed at them by the rest of the men in the carriage.

One guy this year obviously couldn't be arsed to make any sort of effort, and he was holding a daffodil, clearly picked from a park or something, wrapped in some of that blue tissue you get from the work toilets.

Someone is sleeping in the spare room tonight methinks.

Wednesday 15 February

This week is one that all commuters hate. It is half-term. It means parents and their vile offspring are on the train in the morning and evening, taking up seats and annoying people with their puerile conversations about what they are doing/have done.

Even more irritating are those with the children who think shouting everything is perfectly acceptable, and the parents have no concept that their child's voice is penetrating every inch of commuters' souls like a pneumatic drill.

Most commuters have/have had young children, but they are glad to be escaping to get to work, and the last thing they need is someone else's little dears disturbing their morning/evening ritual.

Some drippy mothers whisper 'Shhh, darling', every now and again, but most of them sit there with an indulgent look on their face. I would quite happily wipe that look off their faces with a swing of my rucksack.

Thursday 16 February

Full-blown argument in the carriage this evening between a woman with two ill-mannered, shouty kids, and a regular commuter.

"Would you mind keeping the noise down?" pleads the exhausted commuter after 10 minutes of continuous shouting and shrieking. The sprogs continue to yell at the top of their voices. This exchange happens three times.

Then the commuter just erupts, "Can you keep your bloody children quiet?! This is the quiet coach."

The smug tourist mother replies, "Obviously you don't have children with your lack of patience and understanding."

Commuter replies, "Actually I have three, but I've managed not to be a failure of a parent and teach them some manners and general respect for other people."

Cue some gentle applause. Mother of kids from hell goes red and drags her still-shouting children out the carriage. The silence is heaven.

Friday 17 February

Work from home today so I miss the last day of half-term. After yesterday I am extremely grateful for small mercies.

Monday 20 February

The feeling of desperation when the platform noticeboard keeps updating the 'Expected in ?? minutes' sign and you have been waiting half an hour beyond the allotted departure time already. Over-running engineering works again, apparently. Do the hours run differently on railway time? How can these things constantly overrun? Do the foremen of these crews not possess watches or a basic understanding of the word deadline?

Fire off an email to my boss explaining

that I am going to be late. And I will probably miss the meeting we had scheduled that morning. I'm sure he thinks I'm making it up half the time. I mean, how often can a train be late, right?

Well, I'm NOT. OK? I'm stuck here on a bloody freezing platform, getting wet because I've forgotten my umbrella, and unable to get inside because the meagre waiting room is already rammed with miserable-looking people.

The train arrives forty minutes late, I look like a drowned rat, and as we pull off, I receive a text saying our meeting has been cancelled and I might as well work from home today.

Too. Bloody. Late. I'm on a non-stop service to London. *bangs head against wall*

Tuesday 21 February

The train is on time today. Well it would be wouldn't it? I don't need to be anywhere specific. The train home is also on time. Now I know it is all going to go tits up tomorrow.

Wednesday 22 February

A second day of perfect service. Wow, this

is fab. I feel confident enough to accept an invitation for dinner and drinks out in the city tomorrow night. The train operator has turned over a new leaf. I feel happy.

Thursday 23 February

No they fucking haven't. There is no new leaf. I am an idiot to even think it. I get back to the station this evening after meeting friends for dinner, and discover all the trains home have been cancelled. Again. This is due to some massive signal failure apparently. As usual, there is nowhere to find out information from and time is running out. I check the train company's Twitter feed to see what they are suggesting, and see that they are 'taking a break from Twitter this evening due to unforeseen circumstances'.

Now I am pissed off. I find a poor, harassed-looking employee and ask them what the hell I am supposed to do. They look ready to cry and say they have no idea.

I book into a hotel (get the last room) and sink onto the bed in despair, ringing a friend to ask them if they would go and feed my poor cat.

WHY can't I just be happy with a local job?

Friday 24 February

There is no way I'm going into work wearing yesterday's clothes and even worse, yesterday's knickers. I tell my boss what happened, and tell him I'm going home now and will be working from home.

I get to the station, and the trains are still not sorted properly. It takes me four hours to get home, switching from train to bus, bus to train and finally to a taxi. My boss thinks I am taking the piss and tells me I need to have a report ready for him by the end of the day. It was due at the end of next week.

I call the train company and tell them they have cost me nearly £150 (along with my reputation) and ask where I can reclaim that from. The cheeky sod on the other end actually chuckles and tells me I have no chance of claiming that back. Both cash and reputation, I assume.

"Suck it up Buttercup", he said. Probably.

Monday 27 February

Fuck off. I'm not going into London today.

I got the report done late on Friday evening but I don't know if it made any sense. I am hoping my Wi-Fi reception is as crap as the trains today, and stops any emails from my boss coming through. Sadly, my email works, and I spend the day making corrections and cursing train companies for messing with my brain.

Tuesday 28 February

It is Shrove Tuesday apparently. Sod making pancake batter. I want to batter someone's face for all the hassle over the past few days. Someone from the train company approaches me at St Pancras holding a basket and looking happy. I stare them down until their bottom lip trembles and then I flounce away in disgust. They can stick their crappy pancake wrap thing up their twill-clad arses.

MARCH

Wednesday 1 March

Raining again. And to top it off I forgot my umbrella. Again. Stood outside in the pouring rain and the train guard thought it would be funny not to open the doors for a full five minutes.

Obviously I couldn't get under any shelter because I would lose my place by the door and not be the first to get on the train. That is vitally important in the mornings. Manners count for nothing. I was also eyeing up a bloke with a crutch to my right. If he thinks he can get on first, he can piss right off. Got it, hoppy?

Of course, when the doors were finally unlocked, I let him hop on first with a really sweet and genuine smile and a gentle "After you", as the rainwater ran in rivulets off my nose. I'm not having anyone think I'm rude.

The fucker went and sat in the seat I was heading for. Absolute bastard. That's the last time I fall for the invalid sob story. Push your way on like everyone else, you plaster-covered git.

Thursday 2 March

It's raining again. Seriously? Like trudging to work in the dark isn't shitty enough already, it chooses to constantly piss down as well. I really do need a holiday – I need some sun. I'm going to book one when I get to work today. I won't let the fact that every time my season ticket loan is taken out of my wages, I am reminded it would pay for a week's cruise in the Med get me down. Nope. I am not bitter.

Whoop, I've booked my first holiday. Next month for a whole week. The only downside is that I have to get the train to the airport. On a Sunday. But I'll be fine won't I? The train Gods will be kind to me! I've earned it.

Friday 3 March

A new poster has gone up at the station boasting how my train company had achieved 99.1% punctuality and 99.4% reliability over the past year, to encourage more gullible fools to use their services. I did a double take when I saw it. Really? EVERY SINGLE TRAIN I GET IS LATE. I can vary the times all I like, it makes no difference. Late, late, late.

Which single service are they measuring these stats by? Some ten-mile loop on a seldom-used route way up north? I enjoyed watching people's faces as they caught sight of the poster on their way to the platform. Some laughed out loud. Some tutted. Some swore. One even mouthed "Fuck off" at the poster.

Someone had scrawled 'Bollocks' at the bottom of the poster by the time I got home in the evening. It made me laugh anyway.

Monday 6 March

The poster has been further vandalised over the weekend. Someone had drawn a cock and balls on the main character's forehead and a steaming turd on the floor. Classy.

By the time I got back that evening, the poster had vanished.

Tuesday 7 March

They have closed the buffet car. I repeat. They have closed the buffet car. The shock and outrage on everyone's faces when this announcement was made amused me greatly.

Particularly as none of us even used the bloody buffet car since they stopped the free tea and coffee offer for season ticket holders five years ago. Instead, we will get an 'at-seat trolley service'.

That is going to work so well. Especially when people are packed into the aisles like sardines and bags are scattered all over the floor. I'm sure everyone will be delighted to make way for the trolley. Yup, great idea guys. But apparently we will get more seats in pleb class as a result. Of course we will.

Wednesday 8 March

We were delayed getting on the train this morning because the FRICKING 'refreshments' trolley was blocking the aisles. We had to wait while some aged crone decided whether she wanted a biscuit or a chocolate bar with her ridiculously priced cup of tea.

As more and more people piled on behind me and the door shut, she had moved on to wondering whether perhaps a muffin might be better.

As the train started to move off, I could contain myself no more. "Would you mind letting us all past please so we can sit down?" I politely asked the trolley dolly. The glare I got back would have frozen boiling water.

"GET OUT THE FUCKING WAY", shouted a bloke about a mile back down the carriage. With much huffing and puffing, she reversed the trolley back down the carriage until we could pass.

I never did find out what the old bat ordered in the end. Something covered with powdered arsenic hopefully.

Thursday 9 March

Some vile woman in front of me thought it would be fine to brush her long, tangled hair on the train and then casually throw the bloody great hairball it created onto the floor behind her. It was the size of Cousin It by the time she had finished. UGH! I have a hair phobia and sat there physically gagging and paralysed in fear in the case the thing sprang to life and entangled itself around my legs.

A brave bloke in the seat across from me reached over after we exchanged horrified glances, picked it up (bleurgh), and threw it back in her lap.

"I think you dropped something," he said to her.

She sat there holding the minging hairball until she got off at the next station. I presume she bought it a collar and lead and started calling it Fido.

Friday 10 March

That feeling when you fall into a deep sleep once you leave London and wake up EXACTLY when the train pulls into your station. Oh yeah. Feeling gooood.

Monday 13 March

Sneaky day working from home today. I'm content with hearing the trains rumble past the bottom of my garden and staying well away from the bloody things.

Tuesday 14 March

I had someone's arse in my face the whole journey into work today. A cancelled train meant two loads of people squeezing into one train. No extra carriages of course. "Suffer, you peasants", the train operators chuckled to themselves.

I swear this person let one off as well. As I sat there gasping for air from the pungent smell, he emits a foul-smelling silent burp as well. Lovely. Nice of him to share last night's kebab (with hot sauce) with me.

Wednesday 15 March

On the way home this evening there was a mousey-haired girl with a phoney 'luv you bruv' type faux-urban accent talking loudly on her phone to a mate about her love life. She had her feet on the table and attitude oozing from every pore.

It went something like this (forgive me, I'm not exactly 'down wiv da kids'):

"Yeh, he owned me, innit? I was well derp when I left him hanging with that munter on Saturday night. I bought some sick jeans and a top to show him what he's missing, but he just dissed me when I turned up at his crib last night. Now I'm not sure if I can hang wiv da squad anymore..."

She droned on for over an hour in the same vein.

Sorry, but WTF are you people talking about? Why do you have to talk in that ridiculous accent and suck your teeth like that? You are not living in some sort of ghetto.

The funny thing was, when the conductor asked her for her ticket, she put her phone down and spoke in a perfectly normal accent, quite posh actually, and I'm sure I heard a 'Yah', but she switched straight back to street when he had gone.

Ah, the beauty of yoof. Innit?

Thursday 16 March

After yesterday's entertainment, I wasn't prepared for another girl spilling her life story into her phone so soon. Neither was a bald-headed guy in my carriage. After about fifteen minutes of her loud honking voice (not so much street this time, but reality TV-style dimwit talk with every statement sounding like a question), he strode down the carriage, banged hard on her table, making everyone jump, and slapped his other hand against the window, next to the sign that said 'Quiet Coach'.

"Can you effing read?" he roared.

"Yeah." she replied.

"Well shut the FUCK up then," he said.

She shut the fuck up and moved carriages extremely quickly after that.

Friday 17 March

Wooh! It's St Patrick's Day today! A few people got on the train wearing huge green hats and clutching tins of Guinness this morning. Within a few minutes, they were singing at full volume. More got on at the next two stations – I'm not sure if it was an organised trip, but there was no escaping them.

Some people got up and moved carriages, to a chorus of boos; others, including me, tried turning their headphone volume up. It didn't work. Their volume increased instead. So I just decided to go with it and suck it up.

By the time we got to London, two had been sick, one was comatose in his seat and the others were stumbling around all over the place, ricocheting off every seat as they headed for the exit.

I don't envy them their heads tomorrow.

And I think a London hospital may be getting a visit before too long.

Sláinte!

Monday 20 March

I had just got comfortable in my seat when the train came to a sudden screeching halt outside my station, causing one woman to fly headlong into a luggage rack, and another bloke to fall into a fellow commuter's lap. Tea and coffee was sloshing everywhere.

I think I got whiplash as I narrowly avoided headbutting the seat in front of me. Apparently, a door wasn't closed properly before we left the station. Was there really any need to brake so violently? Surely just a gentle slowdown would have been better.

The train manager came striding down the carriage in his important orange vest and nearly went arse over tit as he slipped on someone's banana that had fallen off a table. They were not happy that their banana had been squashed. I laughed like a drain at that image for the rest of the journey.

Tuesday 21 March

Signal fricking failure. Need I say more? But

I had to show willing. After waiting thirty-five minutes on the platform and when my feet actually starting turning into blocks of ice, I decided to give up. Went home and got all my work done early. Bonus.

Wednesday 22 March

Signal failure. No trains in sight, and the others backed up along the line apparently… wait a minute, this happened yesterday as well – surely the signal was eventually fixed? The hassled-looking station person said yes, but it was a different signal down today.

Oh, well, that's OK then. Good job I don't need to get to work in London or anything. Another day at home. The conversation with my boss went really well. NOT.

Thursday 23 March

Some bastard has stolen the copper wiring from the side of the track. So there are no trains. AGAIN. Seriously? This is beyond a joke. The station announcement said a bus replacement service has been set up to get us to another station where the trains are running normally.

I took one look at the bus – circa 1966

and I don't think the tyres have been changed since then either (I swear I saw canvas) – and then another look at the driver (about ninety-five years old with rheumy eyes and shaking hands) – and decided to stay at home.

My boss really loves me this week. I'm trying not to think of the money I am throwing down the toilet in unused train tickets, but I grab a load of refund forms. Compensation claims galore this week.

Friday 24 March

I'm glad I stayed away yesterday. One of my fellow travellers spent three hours trying to get into London before giving up, and then another made it in, but took five hours getting home due to the bus driver getting lost!

Yep, he missed a turn and ended up stuck on the motorway in rush hour traffic, with an accident closing two lanes for that extra bonus. Good job their livelihood doesn't depend on them getting people from A to B. Oh, hang on…

Monday 27 March

Overrunning engineering works made

my train thirty minutes late today. I mean, seriously people, get some fucking clocks.

If you have between midnight on Friday and 10pm on Sunday to get stuff done, set an alarm so you know when to pack up and get the trains in the right place. And don't try to get too much done at once.

WHAT THE HELL IS WRONG WITH THESE PEOPLE? Anyone would think they got overtime on their overtime…

Tuesday 28 March

That moment when you hear "Excuse me, you are sitting in my seat", and your heart sinks. The reservations are not working, so every seat is fair game. You explain this to Johnny tourist and hope they go away. Wrong. They just stand there. "You are sitting in my seat" they repeat. Practically all the other seats are empty.

Usually I move, but this person and their dogged persistence annoyed me so much I exploded.

"Listen buster, there are no reservations on this train tonight, pick any bloody empty seat and sit down," I ranted.

"I'm going to find the guard," they retort.

Go on punk, make my day. Take your £10 ticket and shove it.

The guard turns up in the still empty carriage and quietly tells the person to sit in another seat because the booking system is not working today.

HA. SCREW YOU SUCKER. I mentally flip him the bird.

Wednesday 29 March

I was late finishing work, so missed my usual train by a minute. I watched its red lights disappear into the distance and wanted to scream. The tannoy announces that there has been an 'incident on the southbound line' and no inbound trains are expected for the foreseeable. Typical.

Two hours later, after being told a train was 'just outside the station', one turned up. The sea of people waiting for it seemed to go on forever. I have never run so fast to get a seat before but I triumphantly plonk myself down. Suddenly, I recognise the shambling gait of the asshole from yesterday making his way down the carriage.

"Excuse me" he says to a 6ft 4 business

man waving his ticket in his face, "you are sitting in my seat."

After repeating himself about five times with no response, he starts tugging on the guy's sleeve.

The man looks incredulous, stands up to his full height, looks the guy in the face and says, "I suggest you fuck off now, before I tear you a new one."

Sleeve-tugger blanches and runs out of the carriage. Bravo!

Thursday 30 March

I saw stars this morning after some clumsy arsewipe banged the corner of his briefcase into the side of my head as he was striding through the carriage. Because holding it under one arm like a newspaper is a really sensible thing to do when the aisles are narrower than Twiggy's hips.

He wasn't going to stop. I actually have a cut on my face.

"Oi you wanker" I scream. "Look what you've done with your stupid briefcase."

He stops dead, comes back, leans down and sneers, "You should have kept your face out the way then."

He goes on his way. This isn't over. I vow to get revenge.

Luckily for me I see him on the way home this evening. As he strides past with his particularly self-important gait, I stick out my foot and he trips beautifully. Unfortunately the fucker doesn't fall over.

He looks back. I meet his eyes and stare him out. He turns away and carries on.

Draw.

Friday 31 March

Classic commuter battle today between a middle-aged woman (no, she hasn't had any Botox, honest) and an older businessman who had both sat at the same table. Well I call it a table, but it is more like a Formica plank. They both dumped their laptops on the table and there was an almighty clash when they opened them up and the screens collided.

"Sorry," they both said at once.

Then I watched as the man ever-so-gently started to try to gain ground by pushing his laptop a little further away from him. The woman pushed back gently.

Ten minutes into this game and the little

pushes are now a lot harder. Finally, the woman snaps. "Do you mind?" she snarls. She then opens her screen even wider. By now a few of us are watching with great amusement.

Fully beaten, the guy spends the next hour meekly contorting his head to the side as he tries to work from his partially closed laptop, while the victorious woman clacks away triumphantly at her keyboard with her painted talons.

APRIL

Monday 3 April

Definitely an April Fools' start to the day this morning. The train was twenty minutes late because of a 'late running crew member'.

Ironically, because one person couldn't be arsed to get out of bed on time, at least 600 other people were now late for work. Cheers for that, you lazy, good-for-nothing fucker.

Tuesday 4 April

Just four days until my holiday – I cannot wait. The train was late again this morning due to a late running crew member. Groundhog Day. Seriously, two days on the trot?

If it was the same person and I were their manager, I would seriously consider perhaps NOT LETTING THEM WORK ON AN

EARLY MORNING COMMUTER TRAIN? FFS, give them an early bonus of an alarm clock, and if that doesn't work, present them with their P45, pronto.

Wednesday 5 April

Luckily our driver this morning managed to get up on time, as the train actually arrived when it should. My journey was made extra pleasurable this morning by an older lady who was clearly having naughty text exchanges, due to her coquettish little 'oohs' and giggles in between each text, which arrived at full volume every couple of minutes.

Each little bleep managed to worm its way under my skull and my nerves until I could stand it no longer. I could see a few people around us raising their eyebrows too. "Please would you mind turning your sound down, it is quite distracting for everyone" I asked politely. "No, I won't hear the phone if I do that" she said. So the bleeping continued all the way to London.

We got our revenge though. As we approached London, twitching in time to her text alerts, we all stood up ready to get off.

She tried to push past a few people to get closer to the door. They were having none of it and closed ranks. Amazing how a person can fill a train aisle with strategically placed arms and legs.

Text that to your lover, bitch.

Thursday 6 April

This morning I sat next to a sleeping woman and managed to doze off quite quickly.

However, two stops down the line, I hear, "SANDRA! IS THAT YOU?" being shouted in my face. I jump a mile in the air when I open my eyes to find a woman's mush right in front of me.

Yes, it was bloody Sandra. And she was wide awake. Big gob sat across the aisle and they proceeded to have a loud conversation for the next twenty minutes with me in the middle, like some kind of hostile, hunched-up sound reflector.

I offered to swap seats with one of them.

"Oh no," they screeched, "we'll get neckache if we sit next to each other and try to talk."

I spot an old copy of the Metro wedged behind my seat table and proceeded to open it out so they could no longer see each other.

Several tuts and some head moves later, I am happily sitting in the window seat vacated by Sandra as she suddenly decided a twisted neck isn't so bad after all. Wise move Sandra.

Friday 7 April

One day to go. Just one. And then I will be on my way to a week of sun and sand. The trains ran fine both ways today – I'm taking that as a good sign for my trip tomorrow.

Saturday 8 April

Remind me never to rely on trains again, even though they stop directly at the airport! I stood on the platform in the freezing weather with my little wheeled suitcase (I know how to wield these things). Weekend engineering works had started early, meaning I had to catch a bus after the first stop.

The bus was late and we had to wait for some woman who had managed to lose her train ticket. After watching her search every crevice and fold of her bag, and proceed to search her various orifices, she admitted defeat and finally got off the bus to a series of jeers and hisses. I was livid. I made check-in by the skin of my teeth and finally got on board the plane.

It was delayed at the gate for two hours due to a problem with one of its doors. You couldn't make it up, could you?

Monday 10 April - Wednesday 12 April

HOLIDAYS!

Thursday 13 April

My cunning plan to return the day before Good Friday was a good 'un. No delays on flights. Sailed through passport control and the airport shuttle bus was just about to leave when I rocked up. Perfect. Then, as usual where trains were concerned, it went pear shaped. I got to the station and glanced at the noticeboard to see that the trains were all on time. Did a mental fist pump.

The train arrived. My fist pump became a face palm - it was four carriages, jam-packed with people from London, and everyone seemed to have a suitcase. They were piled floor to ceiling.

I forced my way on the train with someone muttering "'There is no room'" as I elbowed past him, and stood for the rest of the journey with my face pressed up against the glass partition between the vestibule and the carriage. Welcome back!

Friday 14 – Monday 17 April

EASTER – more holidays!

Tuesday 18 April

In my head I am still on holiday, but sadly this is not the case. Back to waiting on a damp platform, surrounded by miserable faces. Although happily not quite so many familiar faces due to it being the Easter holidays.

A child started screeching "Mummy, the train is coming", and my heart sank. Yep, children on the train once more. Crowds of them suddenly appear on the platform. Note to parents, please try and avoid rush hour. It really would be most considerate of you.

Every carriage today was like a crèche, kids everywhere and the noise was unbelievable. I managed to find a spare seat by a miserable-looking man and tried to think happy thoughts. It didn't work. Every

'Are we nearly there yet?' was like fingernails on a blackboard.

Wednesday 19 April

There was a woman sat in my carriage wearing bunny ears today. No joke. Dressed in business attire, but sporting a pair of white, fluffy bunny ears.

Everyone was terribly British and didn't ask her why she was accessorising her outfit in such a manner, but people could not take their eyes off her. She kept a poker face during the whole journey. I was expecting some kind of flash mob experience, but no. She was alone the whole time.

She was clearly a woman who just liked rabbits. Perhaps a teensy-bit too much?

Thursday 20 April

Dear day trippers, please let me educate you on train door etiquette. When you are standing in the vestibule as the train approaches the station, there is an order to it. If you get there first, you are first to get off the train, second, you are second etc, etc. It is not rocket science.

But there is nothing that pisses me off more than when someone trundles into the corridor and is blatantly going to push in line. Today it was an older couple sporting matching rucksacks and jackets and clutching walking poles (a must in central London). They had eyed me up and down and looked like they meant business, with the bloke ready to push his way off and the woman holding lightly onto his shoulders.

Normally I would fight back, making eye content and generally giving them evils. But I couldn't be bothered. However, the woman fell victim to a stray gust of wind as she got off the train. It pushed the door back and she ended up ripping her North Face walking jacket on the door catch as she squeezed out.

Oh how I fucking laughed at that one!

Friday 21 April

I reached out to open the door this morning and my hand came away sticky. I gagged as I looked up to realise I had just put my hand in someone else's vomit.

The dirty bastard had blown chunks out of the window and it had gone all down the side of the train and all over the window and handle.

Struggling not to vomit myself, I went into the toilet and scrubbed my hands. Felt quite ill all the way to work today!

Monday 24 April

It must be a time for disgusting people to be out in force at the moment. There was a bloke on the train picking his nose and flicking it around. I swear some of it went in a woman's eye as the flick-to-blink and wipe-at-eye ratio was definitely on point.

He must have been doing it for a good ten minutes, rootling around up there to find any strays.

I muttered "You dirty bastard" under my breath, but I think he heard me. The picking stopped.

Tuesday 25 April

As I was waiting by a door for my train to pull into my station this evening, I had the pleasure of listening to well-known local bankers Jeremy and Rupert's conversation about their upcoming retirement plans. Both had been commuting for about 500 years, and were "Bally well looking forward to giving it up".

"What will you do with your time, old boy?" said Rupert, scratching his prominent red drinker's nose.

"Oh, probably retire to our house in the South of France" replied Jeremy, rubbing at a thread-vein pattern on his rosy cheeks.

I hope you make it that far guys. The way they staggered off the train made me wonder if the only place they will be going is a spell at Her Majesty's pleasure for driving their Bentleys well over the limit. I felt drunk from the fumes of just standing near the door with them for five minutes.

Wednesday 26 April

That annoying moment when you wake up from a nice doze and see several people's jaws working ten to the dozen and they are obviously having an argument, but you fail to rip out your earbuds in time and just catch a stray "Fuck you, too," as they storm out of the carriage at the next stop. I hate missing the chance to earhole in other people's misery on the trains.

Thursday 27 April

The refreshment trolley was particularly annoying today as the woman decided to take her time walking up the carriage and say a big fuck you to all the people trying to get on and get a seat.

She then got her revenge on all the moaning and pleas of "Please can you let everyone past?" by coming back down the train at a very fast pace, clipping plenty of elbows and stray feet as she went. From the amount of hissing and gasping, we could have been in the reptile house at London Zoo.

Because she was a shapely lady as well, plenty of others experienced the head/hip rebound as she forced her way through the relatively small gap at speed. I think we all decided never to mess with her again.

Friday 28 April

Same trolley dolly was on the train today, but an announcement came over the tannoy saying our 'on-board customer retail host' will be passing through, and please keep all aisles free of bags etc.

On-board customer retail host? Talk about made-up titles. There was quite a lot of sniggering when that title was first announced, but as soon as she appeared in the doorway, not a sound was made.

I did notice her name was Brenda, and that she had a special badge spelling out her title in all its glory.

What does that make the driver? The on-board train directional manager? And is the conductor the on-board ticket inspection specialist?

It has made me want to go into my office and demand a much more fancy title from my boss too. I know where I'd be told to go.

MAY

Monday 1 May

Bank holiday – whoop!

Tuesday 2 May

I forgot that a bank holiday means extra engineering works on the train line. And, just for a change, they overran today. By forty-five minutes.

By the time I had actually managed to squeeze myself onto a train, I was an hour late, and then it proceeded to get so full as we stopped along the line that I was expecting somebody to pump in a few hundred gallons of olive oil at the final stop so we could be properly canned like sardines. Gasp!

Wednesday 3 May

I decided to walk the length of the train this evening to ensure I alighted right by the exit doors of the station. There is something strangely satisfying about getting this right.

But this meant venturing through first class. Ignoring the glares from the upper echelons of train travel, I crept into a doorway and stood there, trying to look just that bit more arrogant so I'd fit in.

William and Sebastian come to join me and speak to each other in that loud 'hooray Henry voice' we all know so well.

"Just got a call from Portia," one said, presumably referring to one of their wives/ girlfriends. "She said would we mind stopping off on the way home and grabbing them some fags?"

Oooh – lovely. Judging by the way one of them was sniffing, I suspected they would pick up a side order of something else on the way home too. The kind that doesn't come in a can but a little plastic bag.

Thursday 4 May

Happy Star Wars day, fellow commuters. Nothing can put me in a bad mood today.

I even said it to a besuited bloke standing at the platform edge whom I thought needed cheering up.

I know we are not meant to speak to each other in commuter-land, but everybody needs a friendly chat now and again don't they? And who doesn't like Star Wars?

"Sorry, what was that?"

Oh, OK.

As instructed, I fucked off to another part of the platform.

That is the last time I ever initiate a conversation with a fellow commuter.

Friday 5 May

I felt warm for the first time this year. It was lovely. The sun was shining, the sky was blue. It was mild enough to take your coat off and bask in the sunshine. It made you glad to be alive.

However, once on the train, I realised the air con had been stuck on full blast and it was like an arctic scene in there. One guy had gone all Jack Nicholson in *The Shining* and was just sitting motionless with a rictus grin on his face.

By the time we got to London, I couldn't feel my hands, feet or nose, and my teeth were chattering.

That'll teach me for daring to feel warm!

Monday 8 May

We had a bit of a joker as a conductor today.

"If you see anything suspicious on the train such as a lone bag, strange-looking package or even someone smiling, please do report it immediately to a member of the train team, or the British Transport Police."

I hope there isn't a miserable bugger on board who reports him for daring to have a sense of humour.

Tuesday 9 May

On the way home today, I was overwhelmed with the urge to pee. I don't use train toilets usually because I imagine the toilets in hell look quite similar: something wet all over the floor (no desire to find out if it is just water), something slimy near the sink – definitely no desire to see if it is spilled hand soap, and usually about a litre of stale piss and someone's recently deposited log still flapping around in the pan.

Many people take the 'Do not flush the toilet when in a station' sign as a 'Do not flush the toilet, EVER, even under pain of death' diktat.

Tonight's toilet did not disappoint and I decided I would rather just wet myself on the walk home, than risk walking into a hellhole.

Wednesday 10 May

That perfect feeling when you have forgotten your headphones, and all you can hear behind you is the sound of slurping, as two twenty-somethings decide to eat each other's faces off. These people hardly came up for air for the entire journey.

As we headed up the concourse they continued to slobber and slurp over each other, but they failed to notice a wet floor sign, and she went down first, dragging him with her.

They elicited a few 'whoops' from passers-by, before legging it down the escalator and disappearing out the doors.

Thursday 11 May

My friend, the 'on-board customer retail host', was back today. She decided that as she went down the carriage she would read out everything in her trolley in a great monotone voice.

"Sweets, chocolates, teas, coffees, sandwiches, muffins, porridges, crisps, biscuits…" she drawled.

Unfortunately, nobody bought a single thing. With an audible 'tut', she moved to the next carriage and her voice went up a decibel as she recited the same list of tantalising snacks.

I can only image that by the time she got to the front of the train, she was shouting and babbling incoherently and just begging someone to buy something from her bulging trolley.

Friday 12 May

I was delayed on the journey home this evening by a 'broken down' train from *[insert rival company here]*. You never actually see these broken-down trains that cause so much hassle, they seem to just vanish into thin air when you eventually crawl past the supposed scene. And it is always a rival train company's fault, even if their trains don't travel as far down the track. I mean, a driver wouldn't make something like that up, would they?

Monday 15 May

Someone actually refused to take their bags off a seat today so I could sit down. She said her bags "needed to be there". Luckily, I grabbed a seat a couple of rows in front. However, when she tried the same tactic with an angry-looking bloke who got on after me, he looked at her, grabbed her bags, threw them into the luggage compartment and just sat down without another word.

Absolute silence from the woman whose bags had just been tossed aside. I wished I'd had the guts to do the same thing to her, but knew that if I had done, I'd have probably been arrested for aggressive behaviour. I wanted to high five the bloke behind me all the way home.

As I left, they were still on the train. Despite the carriage being almost empty, he did not move from his seat.

They were probably still travelling round the network together weeks later like that lead character from *Collateral*.

Tuesday 16 May

I had a conference today, so caught a stupid o'clock train. It was packed, but spot on time for a change. I felt very confident of arriving in plenty of time so I could throw a cup of tea down my parched throat.

I got down to the Tube and every line was down. I decided to grab a cab, but unfortunately half of London had got there before me.

Two hours later, I made the conference in time for morning refreshments. Brilliant. Does any journey ever go smoothly these days?

Wednesday 17 May

There was a guy on his phone in the carriage this morning – "Yah, yah, well I don't have a dog in this fight mate, so it is up to you."

He then proceeded to tick off nearly every word in the corporate 'bullshit bingo' game, including 'synergy', 'running things up the flagpole', and my personal favourite – 'pushing the envelope'. Have you actually tried pushing an envelope? It is not very enlightening.

By the time he had come off his call, most of us knew what deal he was working on (oil industry), who the major competition was, and how much it was worth.

I considered putting in a bid for it myself, until I realised I didn't have a clue about the oil industry and actually didn't want to.

Phone knob then finished his conversation and proceeded to read his *Financial Times* fully opened, despite the glare from his next-door neighbour.

Thursday 18 May

I got engaged in a classic game of 'armrest elbow battle' today. The guy next to me thought he was going to win by using the 'ram elbows quickly on armrest before she sits down' tactic, but I engaged the 'constant gentle pressure' tactic, until he finally gave up and actually shared the fucking thing like we are supposed to.

Friday 19 May

Platform bingo again today. Passengers move to one platform. Wait. Told to move to another. Move. Wait. Train arrives in station. Everyone rushes to that platform, well apart from a few who are hedging their bets. The tannoy announces that the platform is yet to be announced. Repeat scenario twice as sheep mentality gets the better of people.

The train eventually arrives, people pile off it and start crashing into the waiting crowd, which has surged forward in a desperate bid to grab a seat.

I charge up the platform, pushing anything that moves out my path, until I leap, breathlessly, into a carriage and flop into a seat.

Monday 22 May

Day off. I wake up at 5am, sigh, and go back to sleep.

Tuesday 23 May

A new café has opened up in the station foyer. It has put out some tables and chairs and is giving away free teas and coffees to season ticket holders. Nice touch. I take a sip of my tea and meander onto the platform. After all, the noticeboard said the train was running late.

As I step onto the platform, a whistle blows and my train is ready to leave. I run to the nearest door and start pulling the handle, spilling my free tea all over the place and then dropping it altogether as I pull feebly at the door.

Normally, the guard looks disgusted and just sends the train on its way. This morning he reopened the doors for me and a couple of other distressed-looking people. I realise he is not being nice, he got the time wrong and the train still had another two minutes before it was due to leave.

I resisted the urge to ram his whistle somewhere less prominent.

Wednesday 24 May

The conductor we have nicknamed 'Jobsworth', or 'Jobsie' for short, is on duty today. He goes above and beyond the call of duty to try to catch people out. The sheer joy he evidently feels when someone is caught out is obvious for all to see.

He caught someone today.

A poor little old man.

He had clearly got on the wrong train by accident, but that wasn't enough for Jobsie. He went on and on at him until he broke and coughed up another £25 to upgrade his ticket.

Shame on you Jobsie, shame on you.

Thursday 25 May

All week, we have had people dressed in their

finery going to the Chelsea Flower Show. In what has come as no surprise to any of us Brits, it has pissed down during the day all week. Some of these people are cockier than others, with their VIP passes swinging from their lapels. Most are of a certain age, so there is a lot of crimplene-and-chino-couple-combinations going on.

A bloke today in pristine chinos, blue blazer (with VIP badge proudly displayed) and panama hat, struts onto the train, turfs someone out who is sitting in the window seat at that particular table, with the old "These are our reserved seats" line. Pushes his rather meek looking crimplene-dress-clad wife into the window seat and sits down.

What he didn't realise is that the seat he had reserved had been the scene of a serious coffee spill – not sure if by the guy he turfed out, or a previous occupant. It takes a few minutes, but he leaps to his feet and everyone can see a spreading coffee stain on his arse.

"Bally hell!" he exclaims. "Where is the train manager?"

Guess what? It is Jobsie! I settle in for the entertainment. Many of us who have been trying not to laugh are now very red in the face when Jobsie comes along.

A long and loud 'discussion' ensues, where pompous bloke demands something is done about his trousers – (err, - what exactly? Magic a pair out of thin air?), and then starts demanding compensation for "Making us travel on such a filthy, disgusting train".

Jobsie remains calm throughout and tells the guy there is nothing he can do. Perhaps he should try to wash his trousers in the cloakroom, or buy a new pair.

"So you are going to do nothing?" says coffee-arse, leaning right into Jobsie's face.

"That's right, I'm afraid. Nothing I can do. Accidents happen."

Perhaps if percolator pants had taken up one of the two rows of empty seats in the carriage instead of lording it over someone else in his £10 seats, he would have avoided the issue.

He spends the rest of the journey moaning and muttering to his wife, who, to be honest, looks half dead. Living with him, I'm not surprised.

Friday 26 May

I get to the station extra early. Do not stop at café. Do not grab a drink. Get on train. Train leaves. Get to work.   Repeat on journey home.

Monday 29 May

Another bank holiday – absolutely bloody brilliant!

Tuesday 30 May

Guess what? Overrunning engineering works means my train is thirty-five minutes late. By the time it arrives, the platform is full of annoyed people, me included. We push our way on, there are no sodding seats, so we stand in the aisle. By the time we get to London, and we have had 'MOVE DOWN THE BLOODY TRAIN' shouted at us several times, nobody is able to move and we have to execute a careful manoeuvre to get off the train or we would all have toppled like dominos. Such a pleasure.

Wednesday 31 May

The world's sweatiest man gets on and decides to sit next to me. I am cowering away from him in revulsion. He has clearly cycled to the station, but is literally dripping with sweat. His hair is plastered to his head, and his T-shirt is sodden. He leaves a wet mark on my shirt sleeve as he brushes against me unintentionally. I gag.

As the train pulls off, he starts breathing heavily and I catch the smell of garlic. It is no good, I cannot stand it. I am on the verge of losing my breakfast.

I politely ask to get out, and I rush out of the carriage to stand by the window, breathing deeply with my head stuck outside. I would rather stand for the next forty minutes than sit next to that disgusting creature any longer.

As we pull out of the last stop before London, I sneak a peek to see who is sitting next to him. The sweat is still glistening down his arms, and the seat next to him is empty. I suppose it is one way to get some room in cattle-class.

JUNE

Thursday 1 June

Did I mention it was bloody half-term again this week? Thursday is obviously the day for it. The train was absolutely packed with kids and their smug parents, toting bags filled with healthy treats and snacks. Let's see you later after a few hours of the kids demanding a visit to M&M World, wolfing bags of vile sweets and a dodgy hot dog from a street vendor. You won't look so bloody smug then, I can assure you.

One delightful child thought it would be good to just emit a high-pitched scream at various intervals along the way. Its mother just looked at it and said "Sweetie, don't do that." After the tenth time (not that I was counting), a guy sitting near them just issued his own version of the scream, staring them in the face as he did so.

The child spent the rest of the journey staring at said bloke with its mouth open, and my fellow passengers spent the remaining time trying to bring their heart rates back to normal.

Friday 2 June

It is actually hot today. The hottest day of the year so far and, in fact, of the past 100 years. I was happy to arrive at the station early before we actually started cooking. Miraculously, the train was on time. However, unlike in the middle of winter, the air con wasn't on in any carriage; it was so hot, the air was actually sucked out of your lungs the minute you stepped through the doors.

To top it off, we were delayed for forty minutes because the tracks had 'become warped due to the hot weather'.

Seriously? Steel tracks, forged under tremendous heat, are unable to take the UK summer sun?

One thing that was never in any danger of warping on my train line is the speed at which we travel.

Monday 5 June

Interesting scenario today. It is still half-term somewhere along my line. A small child called Quentin (we know this because the mother coos his name every five minutes) was running up and down the middle of the seats on the way home from work. Said child gets foot caught in the handle of some middle-aged businesswoman's handbag, and goes flying, smashing its face on the arm of a chair. As the melodic screaming begins, the Sloanie mother comes charging down and has a go at the woman for leaving her bag in the way.

The woman retaliates by saying the person should control their "horrible child" and teach it some respect for other people. When she said that, several people murmur their agreement and the mother looks furious, grabs little Quentin and sneaks back to their seat. I heard her promise him a treat when they "Got to Waitrose". Probably a double macchiato.

They get off the train at the first stop, no doubt heading to pick up their Range Rover Evoque in the car park.

Tuesday 6 June

Due to there being a 'reduced train service', we were packed on the train like sardines again this morning, and it was very warm. A bonus was that none of the half-termers could hack the pace and didn't get on.

About ten minutes outside London, the train comes to a sudden halt and we all stumble over one another trying to stay upright. Everyone does their usual and tries to avoid making any eye contact whatsoever, which is quite difficult when someone's eye is so close to yours that you can count the veins.

Forty minutes later I have counted the veins in about ten people's eyeballs, and the temperature in the carriage is reaching Saudi desert levels. There has been no announcement, no information, we cannot get off the train or move anywhere. I can't even hurl insults at them via Twitter, as conveniently there is no reception where we are stuck.

A woman keels over and then we spot movement on the tracks alongside the train. Men in orange gear are chucking bottles of water through the door windows. No joke. Someone actually moves their arse off their seat to let the woman sit down and someone else drags her onto the seat where she slumps mumbling incoherently. Men in orange have no idea what is going on, they shout, they were just told to give out water.

Another twenty minutes later, just when we are all beginning to give up hope, the train moves and we pull into the final station before London, and the doors open. We all tumble outside, sodden with sweat and oozing hate.

"The train is terminating here," whines a nasal voice over the shit tannoy system. "We are sorry for any inconvenience this will cause".

I put my head in my hands and actually wept.

Wednesday 7 June

After yesterday, when it took me four hours to get home again, and yet another day's work lost, I decided I would work from home today. Good move. By starting at 5am, and finishing around 8pm, I managed to catch up on everything. If the trains aren't running tomorrow, I think I will actually cause someone GBH.

Thursday 8 June

The temperature is back to normal. The trains are on time both ways. There is a God. But unfortunately for two blokes, Jobsie is on duty again today. He comes round for ticket inspection and they hand him one ticket. Now, I could swear I heard them talking in fluent English before Jobsie came along, but all of a sudden, they are speaking broken English.

"Where is your other ticket?" asks Jobsie.

"We only need one," says Johnny-not-a foreigner, in his Eastern European accent.

"No, you need one each, and if you fail to buy another one now, we will escort you off the train at the next stop and you will be picked up by the British Transport Police" explains Jobsie. I can see he is beyond excited at the thought of catching someone out.

There is silence for about five minutes as they just stare at each other.

"We not buy another ticket. We have no money" says the second bloke eventually.

"Right, I'm calling the police" says Jobsie, reaching for his walkie talkie and pressing the button.

Amazingly, the first bloke manages to

produce a pretty sizeable wad of notes from his pocket and buys the right ticket, when he realises Jobsie is being serious.

It was all over pretty quickly after that, but Jobsie has a very self-satisfied, smug look on his face for the rest of the journey.

Friday 9 June

Just when I thought the week would end smoothly, we get the classic Friday evening fuck-up of a service. Two stops from home, we learn a broken-down freight train is blocking the line (the only sodding line leading to my hometown) and there is no sign of it moving. So much for my dinner plans tonight with my friends, by the time I get home they will be going to bed.

We start going backwards to the station we left about fifteen mins earlier and are told we have to get off. A bus service has been laid on. My heart sinks. We pile out the door and of course there is no sign of a bus. The train we were just on disappears back in the direction of London.

We wait for the bus.

The original train we were on returns forty-five minutes later, it is packed and we are told it is continuing to my stop after all. Another wonderful trip in the luggage vestibule ensues, with me desperately trying not make eye contact or touch anyone.

Monday 12 June

Heart-stopping moment on the train today. Jobsie wanted to inspect every single ticket in minute detail and I couldn't find mine anywhere. I fumbled around my bag getting hotter in the face, mumbling "It is in here somewhere" and all around me I can see people thinking I am trying to dodge the fare.

"NO!" I want to scream. "I'VE BEEN PAYING FOR MY EXTORTIONATE SEASON TICKET FOR OVER 16 YEARS!"

He does the classic "I'll come back", looking at me like I'd been scraped off his shoe.

Finally, my fingers close on the cheap plastic covering of my ticket. I'd put it in a different compartment of my rucksack for safekeeping because the other one was looking a little worn.

When he comes back, I thrust it at him with a smug look on my face.

He barely looks at it.

I wish I hadn't bloody bothered now. Jobsworth.

Tuesday 13 June

I'm all in favour of getting comfortable on the train. Relaxing and feeling at home. But when a bloke with skinny legs that look about two metres long comes and sits next to me, my heart sinks. This particular daddy-long-legs-esque specimen decides to 'manspread' in the worst way possible. His bony knee is pressing into the side of my leg and forcing me to sit at an angle.

Finally, after forty minutes of pressing back against the onslaught, my shaking muscles can stand it no longer. I turn to him and say very politely, "Is there any way you can move your leg away from me please, mine is turning numb?"

He sits hunched up like a dead spider for the rest of journey, occasionally glaring in my general direction.

Wednesday 14 June

Today is the day I ended up on crutches. To cut a long story short, as I'm waiting to get off the train in London, a bloke who is obviously far more important than the rest of humankind pushes past me at the door and knocks me off balance. I actually know who he is, or at least I have seen him before. I fall the two feet from the door to the platform, twisting my knee in the process. An old cruciate ligament injury is resurrected with a twang and I lay on the floor hissing in agony.

This is what I love about commuting. About fifteen people pile off after me and don't even stop to help, one steps on my bag in his haste to leave. He doesn't even turn around when I croak "Wanker" at his retreating back. Just as I am close to tears, a really nice guy comes up to me and asks if I need a hand. I really did!

I manage to get back on a train that is just leaving, thanks to a very kind guard at the station, and get to my local hospital in one piece thanks to a great taxi driver. Bandaged up, I am told to rest my leg for the rest of the week and to 'be more careful'. Yes, I really did this on purpose, doctor. I am given crutches to hop around on for a few weeks which I have to use while I heal.

I tell you what, if I see that ignorant moron who pushed me over, he will need crutches for the next six months.

Thursday 15 and Friday 16 June

I am housebound due to my knee injury after a four-hour stint in casualty last night. I spend a lot of time with my knee elevated and covered with an ice pack, dreaming up ways of getting my own back on the arsehole who pushed me off the train in their own self-important rush. You will be mine, you utter fucker.

Monday 19 June

I pity anyone who is disabled and who tries to use my train company from my home station.

For a start, the platform is so damn low, you need a stepladder to reach the train step, and that is without the crutches.

Stick those into the equation and you are in a losing battle.

Despite the usual scrum around the door, a very kind man lets me get on first, and with some careful timing, I manage to get on the step.

I've chosen the carriage that I know has a seat that allows extra room for people in my situation, but when I get to it, a snotty-looking woman with the look of Kim Woodburn about her and reading the *Daily Mail* (say no more) has her bag on the seat.

"Excuse me, do you mind if I sit there please?" I ask politely.

"Why can't you just sit in that empty seat behind?" she snaps without even looking up.

I gently raise my crutch and wave it in front of her before pointing to the sign that says seats reserved for elderly and 'less able'.

"Would you please move your bag?" I ask.

She looks in disgust at me and my crutches and actually gets up to sit somewhere else, flouncing past me.

A guy who has been waiting patiently behind me mutters "Silly bitch" as he walks past her. He is my new train friend. Unless he was talking about me? Oh God. Was he? Commuter paranoia!

Tuesday 20 June

I think it must be Ladies Day at Ascot today - there is a gaggle of women on the train this morning wearing the most ridiculous hats and some of them have dresses on that barely cover their modesty.

One has what looks like a lobster on her head and another has what looks suspiciously like a picnic basket with yet another in some sort of silver bucket contraption. Perhaps they are resorting to African methods of toting their food supply for the day on their heads. Some of the hats have feathers sticking out at all angles, and a bloke sitting behind them keeps rubbing his head as the feather brushes it, which is pretty amusing.

However, the best bit is when one decides to get up on her ten-inch heels to go to the loo. Just as she is walking past, the train gives a violent lurch to one side and over she goes.

"Aw FOOKING HELL" she screams as she tumbles. Classy these birds. But at least she is wearing knickers - we all got an eyeful.

Someone asks her if she is ok and if she needs a hand. "Do I look fooking OK?" she yells.

She is hauled back to her feet and limps back to her seat looking like she has just been dragged through a hedge backwards, as the fall dislodged her hat and caused her hair to just collapse.

I wonder what they will be like when they have a few bevvies inside them later on?

I watch them all totter off the train in London as I hobble along on my crutches and wonder which one will go over on her ankle first. Ouch.

Wednesday 21 June

It's the longest day of the year today – quite depressing when you think the nights are going to start getting shorter again.

Quite a few hippy types got on the train at my station today, they were obviously on their way down south to celebrate.

The carriage smelt of incense and something else I won't mention, but needless to say I felt pretty mellow all day. Peace, man.

Thursday 22 June

Yep, the day definitely felt shorter today. Shame the journey each way was lengthened by about forty minutes due to 'trackside equipment failure'. Trackside equipment what now?

This is one of my favourite excuses because it actually doesn't mean anything to the average commuter and we have to just sit there and nod like we know what they are talking about.

Friday 24 June

After someone told me to "get a move on" as I was hobbling up the aisle today, I was just about to lose my shit and was certainly in no mood for the Tube today.

The line I have to use has absolutely no escalators down to the platform, it is all steps, and you can imagine how slowly I moved. I could hear people tutting and moaning behind me as I inched my way forwards.

However, when I finally managed to get on the Tube, what a difference. Despite it being packed, three people offered me their seat, and one guy asked if I wanted to lean against the wall where he had been standing. As someone who is phobic about any germs, this seemed like my best bet.

Felt really buoyed getting off that train.

Fast-forward to the evening service when I was back with my fellow commuters. I was left behind in the scram to get on the train, and a few of them just left bags etc in the aisle as I hobbled up to a spare seat.

I spotted the arsehole who pushed me over though and got my own back by managing to get my crutch right on top of his foot and pressing all my weight on it as I was passing. I'm not a dainty person, and I got a satisfying wince, before I said in a really insincere and high-pitched voice "Oooh, sorry".

HA, you fucker! There's more where that came from as well.

Monday 26 June

It's hot again today. After weeks of 'meh' weather, it feels hotter than Hades. I just want to stay at home in the garden and enjoy the sunshine, but instead I cram myself (and my remaining one crutch – I have ditched one) onto a sweaty metal tube and head down to London, where it is always warmer than anywhere else in the country.

True to form, the air con is not switched on in any carriage. And trust me, I hobbled the length of the train to find some air. I sit next to a guy who has obviously been sweating for a few hours. Every time he moves, I get a whiff of his particularly pungent odour.

It feels like the longest journey in history, and by the end of it my eyes are watering and I have no mascara left. I get outside and take great big gasping gulps of air like a fish suffocating, but I think a film of his sweat has settled inside my nasal passage. I can still smell it two hours later. Gag!

Tuesday 27 June

My favourite trolley dolly – oops, on-board customer retail host – excelled herself today. She managed to spill a cup of lukewarm tea over not just one person, but a whole table full of people this morning. To make it worse, they were loud, clearly retired and had very little of interest to talk about.

No amount of apology on her part, or the offer of a free cup of tea, would placate this miserable lot, so she did the sensible thing and just left them to it.

The rest of us had to sit there listening to these people moaning for the rest of the journey that they are wet through and that their day has been ruined. One even phoned a friend to tell them about 'teagate'. It is just a bit of tea, FFS.

They didn't think that by constantly whining and moaning about a little warm liquid being splashed on their crimplene and nylon outfits, they were ruining the morning of around 100 other people in the carriage at the same time.

Wednesday 28 June

It must be the week for cyclists. A guy today gets on the train in full lycra, Ray-Bans and a fancy schmancy helmet. He is definitely an older guy, judging by the grey chest hairs poking through the lycra.

He heads to the luggage rack in the middle of the carriage and then proceeds to strip off his neon yellow sweatshirt, T-shirt and wife-beater vest, before sponging himself down with a disgusting looking stained sponge that he had in his rucksack and soaked with water from his canteen.

A lot of people are looking on open-mouthed as he gives himself a through scrubbing (including between his legs) and then proceeds to spray almost a whole can of deodorant over himself. The choking begins around him and then spreads as the noxious cloud moves down the carriage.

As everyone gasps for air, he puts his clothes back on, grabs his stuff and walks down into ANOTHER CARRIAGE. Probably to get some non-toxic air. What an absolute tool.

Thursday 29 June

Another scorcher today. Again, I wish I could be anywhere but on my way to work. This time, as we get on the train, we are met with a blast of air so cold it would have frozen bubbles. The air con is definitely working this morning. By the time we get to London, everyone is blue with cold and barely able to stagger out into the sunlight.

On the way back, the train has clearly been left in the sun for a number of hours. It was boiling. There was no air con, and the windows could not be opened. I arrived back home sweating and desperate for a cold shower.

I think I'm going to send the boss of my train company a thermometer with the bearable temperatures in summer and winter marked out in bold red lines, with instructions to stick said thermometer into an appropriate orifice when the message has finally sunk in.

Friday 30 June

I had a work event last night so stayed over. I had the hangover from hell on the way home tonight and fell asleep with my earphones jammed in. I must have had a sixth sense working in my favour as I woke up and the carriage was completely empty.

I yanked my earphones out to hear a 'final call' for passengers to disembark the train before it returns to London. Yep, there was a problem on the line and we were all being chucked off early and sent home on a bus.

I moved faster than I ever have in my life, jumped off the train and ran outside the station onto a bus that was just about to leave. Remembered I had left my crutch on the train as we were pulling off. My knee starts to throb.

I glared at all my so-called 'fellow' travellers. Some of them had the grace to look ashamed. Why didn't any of them wake me to tell me what was happening? I will remember this, people.

JULY

Monday 3 July

One more week to go and I have two whole weeks off – absolutely amazing! The countdown is definitely on. No-one has handed in my crutch, which I reported to every lost property office along my route. I'll be charged by the hospital for the bloody things if I don't find it, and they are bright blue! Not easily lost.

The way home today was great fun. We came to a screeching halt at the first station on our route and sat there for thirty minutes. The doors were locked, there was no air and it was getting fairly warm in there.

An announcement is finally made that we are waiting for an ambulance because a passenger has been 'taken ill' on board.

There is a guy in front of me who keeps looking at his watch, sighing loudly and tutting. This is repeated every five minutes. Seriously mate, take a chill pill, we are stuck. Get over it. I'm sure the passenger would rather not be ill.

Said ambulance eventually turns up - we can see the blue flashing lights, and our heads are craning at the windows to see what is going on.

Fifty minutes later we are back on our way again, and we are told via the carriage grapevine that a woman had been severely injured by a wheelie case that had fallen from one of the overhead storage shelves.

Ouch. Those wheelie cases really should be banned. They are a menace. I could rant about them all bloody day.

I hope you make a full recovery, lady.

Tuesday 4 July

Wheelie cases aside, one of my biggest dislikes on a train is someone who comes booming into the carriage, treating it like their office. We had one such dickhead in today. The conversation went as follows:

"Hi, Cynthia?"

[*Cynthia obviously being his PA, or a downtrodden colleague*]

"Yah, can you make sure the Peterson file is ready for when I come in? We are going to close that £10 million deal today..."

[*Cynthia - probably making V signs at the phone- obviously says yes*]

"Oh, and Cynthia, book me a table – my usual one – at The Ritz and tell them to have the champagne on ice. I have some celebrating to do. Ha ha ha."

[*By now Cynthia is probably envisioning cutting off his extremities and shoving them somewhere dark and damp*].

Said idiot hangs up and glues the phone back to his ear.

We are then treated to conversations with Roger, Michael, Keith, Trevor and Tony, and learn that he is due to take a 10% cut of the profits and is "probably going to take a month or two off to spend on my yacht in the Bahamas."

Does this moron think he is invisible? Does he think nobody else can hear him? And most importantly, does he realise that nobody gives a shit about his deal or his yacht (which is probably just an inflatable dinghy)?

One thing is for sure, I will be praying for freak weather in the Bahamas the week he goes out there (oh yes, we know when that is too), but only in the immediate region of this utter braying idiot.

On the way home this evening, I get an email saying my crutch has been handed in. Bloody marvellous.

Wednesday 5 July

I think we had a tropical storm this morning. I have never seen rain like it. The inside of the train was also wet due to people's coats and umbrellas dripping everywhere. Everything smells damp, and nobody should ever have the scent of damp train seat in their nostrils.

Plus, to cap it all, it is Wimbledon fortnight, so this is set to go on for at least two more weeks.

That heady combo of urine, faeces, vomit, sweat, stale food and other vile substances engrained in the seats and carpets is magnified when wet, and the smell becomes unbearable.

Couple that with the 'never cleaned out' bathroom and you could bring out a new fragrance: 'Eau de train' – I think Kiera Knightly or Nicole Kidman would do a great job advertising that.

Thursday 6 July

I try walking normally today. There is no pain in my knee whatsoever, but as I get halfway down the hill to the station, I realise why I need a crutch. I hobble back and grab the remaining crutch. By the time I reach the station I've missed two trains, because amazingly they were on time. The one day I need the trains to be late and they are on time. Oh hello, Mr Law of Sod yet again.

I catch the next train and settle into an extra legroom aisle seat.

At the next station, I am prodded by an old crone in a mac and headscarf telling me to "get out the seat, it is for elderly and less abled passengers".

I show her my crutch (that could be so badly misread) and shrug apologetically.

"Sorry I have a bad knee, so I have to sit here" I say politely (in my head I just mouth "eff off").

She stands there huffing away, despite there being several empty seats in the immediate vicinity.

"Would you like to sit by the window?" I ask her.

"No, I want to sit there" the old bag insists.

"Well I'm sorry, but I have to sit here so I can get up on my good leg."

She goes and fetches the conductor, claiming that I'm refusing to move and am sitting in the wrong seat. It is the nice conductor who everyone likes! And he likes commuters too!

I explain my predicament to him.

He rolls his eyes and says to me, "Madam, would you mind coming with me? I've got a nice seat in first class with your name on it."

The look on the old hag's face is priceless. Up yours, prune face.

I picked up my missing crutch from lost property this evening. I have a matching pair once more!

Friday 7 July

Still revelling in the wonder of my first-class upgrade yesterday, I almost turn left instead of right when I get on the train this morning.

I glance across the aisle after I have sat down and see a woman with a white splotch across her top lip.

She had forgotten to take the cream off when 'de-hairing' her top lip!

"*Oops!*" I think.

However, I soon realise that it is no accident. She begins to apply a full-on face mask, much to the astonishment of the people sitting all around her. I remembered I had some cucumber in my sandwich and nearly offered it to her for her eyes.

She sits calmly with her face-mask on until we are about twenty minutes outside London, then peels it off and squashes it up into a ball before leaving it on the table in front of her.

The look of horror on the bloke's face opposite her is an absolute picture.

By the time we pull into London, she has a full face of make-up and neatly coiffed hair.

As we get off, she leaves the facemask remnants on the table. What a lovely present for the poor people who have to clean the train!

Monday 10 July - Friday 22 July

Two whole weeks off!! Yes! No commuting for two whole weeks.

However, during my holiday to Italy, I decide to use trains to get me between cities.

From my base (about an hour's car drive away from Rome), I get a train to the capital and it costs me €12 for the whole journey, including underground.

The train turns up bang on time, it is clean, there are seats and we arrive dead on schedule. Coming back late at night, the train is waiting on the platform and it deposits me at my local station at exactly the time it said it would.

I decide to take the train to Pisa a few days later – roughly a ninety-minute trip away on rails.

Same thing happens. Ticket is under €15 return, and the train is punctual both ways.

Wow. How did we get it so wrong?

But don't worry, the smugness of the Italian train system soon wore off when I caught a train named after a certain London airport when back in the UK.

An obscene £35 for a one-way fifteen-minute journey. The train was late, it was packed, and to top it off, it was absolutely filthy.

Welcome home, sucker.

But in better news, the crutches have gone for good!

Monday 24 July

I am not quite sure where those two weeks went. But I am aware that my train is packed with families heading to London for a day out. Oh yes, the wonderful school summer holidays are back and now it will be six weeks before we get back to normal.

One set of kids did that lovely thing where they decide to sing all the songs from their last assembly of the year in their loudest and most high-pitched voices.

The parents and grandparents sitting with them give them a round of applause after each song, and the rest of us just sit there in stunned silence as the songs get progressively worse, and louder.

Note to parents who travel at rush hour:

Your kids may be cute. TO YOU. To the rest of us, they really are not. If you must travel at this time in the morning, kindly plug them into a tablet or make sure they knock back a stiff brandy before boarding so they are asleep and quiet for the whole journey. We do not want to hear them sing, see them dance, or hear them shout.

That way, the murderous stares you receive from most of your fellow passengers (even those with children) may not be so intense.

And instead of moaning about people who appear to be tutting, perhaps ask yourselves WHY they are tutting.

They are about to spend the next eight hours crammed on the Tube to get to work, stuck in an office, back on the Tube and then back on the train. All the while wishing they were somewhere else.

Oh, and in this case, buy your tone-deaf children singing lessons as quickly as possible.

Tuesday 25 July

It is a particularly quiet day on the trains today. Absolute bliss in other words. Nobody is sharing a seat with anyone, we all have two to ourselves. But you know what is coming? Yep, two stops from the end we are joined by…a stag party!

They are all dressed as hipsters – it is actually quite funny. The groom is wearing a top hat with a ribbon tied on it saying 'Groom to Be' – it has clearly been made by his mum.

By the end of the journey, the cries of "Get -innnnnn" and "Yeah boi" are not so amusing anymore and they have managed to spill two cans of beer all over the floor and all over one bloke's laptop bag.

He is not a happy camper. After mopping it up, he is sitting there with it clamped to his chest while the stags keep shouting "Sorry mate" at him at regular intervals.

There is a stampede of suits to get off the train in London!

Wednesday 26 July

I arrive at the station this morning feeling hopeful. I notice the crowds of people everywhere, the empty noticeboards and the harassed-looking staff.

I stay for ten minutes and am told there has been a 'fatality on the line'. We have been there many times.

I turn around and go home again.

It is genuinely awful that anyone feels desperate enough to jump in front of a fast-moving train, but it is extremely risky to do it in front of one of ours. The likelihood is that they will be going so slowly, they will only give you a nasty bump.

Unfortunately for this poor individual, he got 'lucky'. Not so lucky for the poor driver.

Thursday 27 July

So this week it is Hooray Henley. There haven't been that many people going to be honest, but today we had a classic – striped jacket and flannel trousers, plus a straw hat. The train was absolutely packed today, so he had nowhere to sit. Luckily for him (not his wife who he left squashed against the door), he had brought one of those ridiculous folding seats that you balance on the ground with a spike, just in case you fancy a sit down between watching Lycra-clad men and women rowing up and down a river.

He decides to make use of his seat for some unknown reason, and sits down declaring loudly and smugly, "I don't need a seat, I've got my own."

Well, guess what happened? The train went round a bend and because all he was balancing on was a ridiculous spike, he went straight over on his side, falling onto a paper carrier bag filled with cut flowers that another passenger had brought on.

"MY FLOWERS!" she screamed. "LOOK WHAT YOU HAVE DONE, YOU IDIOT."

He is still scrambling around on the floor like a complete twat. His (obviously) long-suffering wife pulls out her purse and gives the woman £20, mouthing "sorry" at her.

She then looks at her writhing, floor-bound husband with a look of utter disgust.

Somehow, I think his chair spike may be stored in an alternative place by the end of the day.

Friday 28 July

Lucky me. We are getting to finish work early today as part of a new work perk for the summer.

I make it to the station for 3.30, and wait for the 4.15 train.

Big mistake.

It is a Friday, everyone is travelling home with ginormous bags and the train is just four carriages long. Every seat is fucking booked.

The next one isn't for an hour.

I stand there, sweating profusely in the vestibule area with a sweaty bloke on one side of me and a B.O.-drenched woman on the other.

Oh, what a marvellous start to the weekend. It puts me in such a great mood for the evening ahead.

Monday 31 July

I am working from home today after I cleverly check the National Rail site before getting out of bed, and see that our friend 'over-running engineering works' has reared its ugly head yet again. Sod that for a game of soldiers. My boss barely makes a sound when I ring him to say that I'll be working from home.

AUGUST

Tuesday 1 August

August is my favourite month of the year to travel. It is always quieter in the mornings, and I usually take a few days off because my industry is usually quieter too due to holiday season. What is not to like?

The weather is lovely today, and amazingly the trains both ways were a pleasant temperature as well. If only it could be this smooth every day.

Wednesday 2 August

So, it was a little cooler this morning than yesterday and of course the train carriage's air con was on full blast the whole way to London. The only sound I could hear was the multiple clicking of teeth as everyone sat there dressed in short sleeves and skimpy items of clothing in anticipation of it warming up later on. (Which it did. Outside.)

We asked the train manager if there was any chance of turning it down and he said he would see what he could do at the next station.

The answer, folks, was nothing. He did nothing. Probably sat there in his little train office laughing and sticking two fingers up at us. The absolute shitwad.

I felt sorry for the woman next to me, she had bought a cup of tea from the trolley dolly, and within twenty minutes it had a covering of ice on the surface. She spilled most of it on her lap as her shaking hands could not cope with holding the cup.

By the time we had got to London, everyone was blue with cold and shivering violently.

For once, my tropically heated office was a welcome relief.

Thursday 3 August

Last day in the office for a couple of days, so I was delighted that on my return journey home, the train was delayed due to a 'catastrophic' power failure earlier in the day.

No-one actually explained what they meant by catastrophic, but it was catastrophic. Also, no clue when the trains would start running, but considering it happened in the morning, there was some hope that a train might suddenly appear. It didn't.

The tannoy started up with three very loud notes, and we all prepared for the information. As soon as the person on the microphone started talking, the volume dropped to below audible levels, and you could see everyone straining to hear what on earth was said.

"Did you hear that?" I asked my neighbour. "Not a bloody word" he replied. Everyone had the same blank look on their face.

Someone asked a person in uniform behind the information desk if they could relay what the tannoy message said.

"Sorry, no. Everything was said in the last announcement" the 12-year-old behind the counter said.

"Any chance you could just repeat it, sonny?" said an angry-looking bull-necked man.

"Err, sorry, I don't have access to their scripts," said pre-teen.

"Do you have access to a brain?" asked the angry man.

We all hung around as someone who had tried to get on a neighbouring train service had come back and said tickets were not being accepted.

FIVE HOURS later, I rolled in through my front door. Train, bus, train, bus was the pattern of my story. I can't talk about it right now as I need to lie flat in a darkened room.

Friday 4 August

Day off and not a train in sight. Perfect.

Monday 7 August

Guess what? The trains were delayed again this morning by over-running engineering works. WTF is wrong with these idiots who are supposedly in charge of rail works? Are they totally incapable of sticking to any sodding deadline at all? Have they heard of time management and planning? WHY is it impossible for them to finish on time? Why does it keep happening?

We crawled slowly towards London, as the train manager, one of my favourites due to his incessant babbling during the journey, constantly apologised for the 'inconvenience' caused and repeated that it was due to overrunning engineering works.

I texted my boss to tell him that I would be late for the morning meeting and received a 'whatever' reply back.

Dear train company, if I lose my job because of your constant incompetence, you are going to PAY, you hear me?

Tuesday 8 August

We were delayed this morning about halfway into our journey, by a lorry hitting a bridge. I think some lorry drivers need more regular eye tests. If they are driving a honking great lorry and they are faced with a low railway bridge, there is a pretty good chance that their vehicle will not fit underneath it, no matter how tightly shut their eyes are.

Perhaps they should check a fucking map and take an alternative route that doesn't involve a railway bridge that was built years before their monster trailers were even a thing. Luckily for us the bridge didn't collapse, and after it was inspected and declared safe, we were allowed on our way once more. Just a short fifty-minute delay today.

Wednesday 9 August

Another train driver strike today. Just bloody brilliant. This time it is going on for the rest of the week. Luckily, some of the train managers have agreed to drive the trains for the week, but are warning it was not really 'advisable' to travel.

Some of us don't have a fricking choice. It is either get into work or collect your P45. There is only so far a 'flexible working' policy will flex.

Despite it being August, the four carriage – yes, fucking FOUR CARRIAGE – train was absolutely rammed by the time it got to us.

I managed to find a space to stand miserably for the next hour or so.

One woman was sprawled out comfortably on the floor, legs all over the place, but no one had the guts from my station to challenge her. We prefer to just glare and seethe inwardly.

Some bloke from the next station had no worries. He just trod straight onto one of her legs and when she said, "Oi, watch where you are going you twat."

He replied: "Get out the fucking way then, you stupid bitch."

Oh! It makes me so happy to be part of humanity when you hear such pleasant exchanges between human beings every day.

Thursday 10 August

We had FIVE carriages today. Yes. FIVE. I was still stuck in the corridor next to a stinking toilet, though – what the hell do people DO in those things? Store their waste for the week and just dump it in there from a bucket? Because that is what it smells like.

On the way back, it was a total scrum to get to the train. I was fighting shoulder to shoulder with a bloke at the barrier – we had our teeth bared and were leaning forward in anticipation.

When the barriers opened, I managed to push him just enough so I got through first. Then I did my Usain Bolt impression to get to the train itself and grab a seat.

By the time we left London, I had somebody's arse right in my face again and the guy next to me had a classic case of manspreading.

What a pleasant journey home that was. I resembled a piece of origami by the time

I got off the train in my efforts to maintain some personal space.

Friday 11 August

Back to four carriages. The bastards are still on strike. How selfish can you get? And don't quote customer safety at me, you fuckers.

On a positive note, I beat someone to a luggage rack today which was an absolute victory. He was absolutely livid to have lost out to a woman. Although your legs go numb because the metal rack is not really designed to be a comfortable seat, it is a seat all the same and beggars cannot be choosers. Days like this make my nearly £8,000 ticket so worthwhile. The look on Mr Loser's face was priceless.

Monday 14 August

There was a little woman standing on the platform with a bloody great double bass case today. It was twice the size she was.

I did wonder where on earth she was going to put it once she had actually managed to get it on the train.

Not one person offered to help her, they all pushed past and left her to it.

"Excuse me, do you need a hand with that?" I asked.

"Nobody touches my double bass but me" she answered.

Right. Fine. I also pushed past her and left her to it. Some people!

Tuesday 15 August

That moment when you look around the platform and see about fifteen eight-year-olds in bright hi-vis tops, and you fear that they will be in the same carriage as you. Well, I was determined it wasn't going to happen to me.

I cunningly headed for the back of the train when it arrived, and the carriage is wonderfully empty with just a few scruffy suited men sat there. So far so good.

Five minutes into the journey, I see a flash of yellow. The whole fucking lot come tumbling into my carriage, shrieking at the tops of their voices.

I watched one man just put his head in his hands and stay like that for the rest of the journey.

It is carnage in there. Screaming, shouting and getting het up. And that is just the commuters. The kids are having a great time. I watch the teachers sneak off into another carriage for a good half an hour. They creep back as we pull into London.

My head is ringing by the time I get to London. I give a good glare at the teachers before disembarking, but they couldn't give a shit. Their journey in a different carriage was peaceful as you like.

Wednesday 16 August

On the way home, the lights in the carriage go out suddenly.

"*Absolute bliss,*" I think, and settle down for a nap.

Five minutes later, the train manager comes bumbling in and orders us all out of the carriage.

"We have to lock this carriage off, because it is dangerous having no working lights. Someone may trip or fall. Please move into the next carriage" she says, officiously.

It is still bright sunshine outside. We do not need any lights to see what we are doing.

The train is packed. There are many of us from my home station and we do not fancy standing in a corridor for half an hour when there are plenty of seats where we are.

We refuse to move en masse and stage a sit in.

"What are you going to do about it luv?" shouts one. "We promise not to move, or hurt ourselves in any way if you let us stay."

"I am being ordered by head office to close this carriage, and that is what I will do" she said.

Unfortunately for her, nobody moved, and we spend the next thirty minutes asking why this ridiculous policy is allowed.

The train pulls into the station and the whole carriage empties.

"There you go, my dear, now you can close it off" said one polite older gentleman.

"Oh, I told head office what had happened, and they decided to keep it open" she replied.

Something told me that wasn't the case, but she didn't want to admit she had been beaten.

Passengers 1. Train company 0.

HA!!

Thursday 17 August

There is a bloke sitting in the carriage as bold as you like, eating a packet of crisps.

"What is wrong with that?" I hear you ask. Absolutely nothing.

Until you realise that the dirty bastard is wiping his greasy hands on the seat next to him every time he picks up a crisp. He has a serviette between his knees. Clean and unused.

Some poor sucker is going to have to sit on that seat and will wonder why their arse looks like the scene of a major oil spillage.

I watch in disgust as he continues to do this every time he eats a crisp. When he is finished, he gives the seat a final wipe with his hands, then picks up the serviette and blows his nose.

Lovely. His mother would be so proud.

Friday 18 August

I had to catch a really early train this morning, so the people on the platform all looked like aliens to me.

When you commute, you make 'train friends'. You have no idea of their name (or if they have told you, you have forgotten and you are too embarrassed to ask again) but you know their faces really well, and you say hello and pass commentary on the weather etc every day. You know where they sit and they know where you sit. All is good.

When you take a different train, you are 90% likely not to see anyone you recognise and you have no idea which seats people gravitate towards. You can feel them glaring at you for daring to be on their train because inevitably you will sit in one of their seats.

I could feel the eyes of a particular grey-haired man boring into me all the way to London.

Clearly I was in 'his' seat, but there was not a damn thing he could do about it. Them's the breaks.

Monday 21 August

Four more days to go until a wonderful long weekend – bring it.

Someone on the train today has a terrible case of gut rot.

Every couple of minutes, they release another fetid blast and it seems to hover in the air for an eternity.

I try to see who is doing it, but everybody looks so innocent. I catch another woman glancing round with a look of disgust on her face, and we have a silent conversation.

My look says, *"This revolting stink is nothing to do with me."*

Hers says, *"Me neither."*

I suddenly spy movement out of the corner of my eye and watch as a young bloke, wearing very pointy shoes, lifts a butt cheek slightly and lets another one go. He doesn't have a care in the world, unlike the poor people all around him.

This one is so bad, I have to leave the carriage and stand by the door. It opens and I get a rush of blissfully fresh air.

I hear a little girl who just got on say in a very loud voice as she is walking past with her mother, "Mummy, that man smells really bad. Like poo."

"Sssh darling, don't be rude" whispers the mother.

He turns bright red and heads towards the toilet for the rest of the journey. Well done, kid. You have saved everyone's lungs today.

Tuesday 22 August

Boy, it is hot today. I really do want to just skive off work and sit in my garden. I make it to work, and it is so hot that our air con has packed up, and at 2pm we are all ordered home.

For once, the trains are on time and I get home to enjoy a few hours in the sun. Just what the doctor ordered. I just wish I'd taken a duvet day in the first place. Damn my conscience!

Wednesday 23 August

It is raining today. And when I say raining, I mean more like torrential buckets. I arrive at the station sopping wet. The station floor is like an ice rink. I'm sure they pick those vile yellow tiles because they are the most likely to send an irritating commuter arse over tit before they have a chance to complain.

When we get on the train, everything is wet. The floor is soaked where people have been dripping over it, and most of the seats have wet patches on them. It really doesn't look very good and it smells like wet dog.

Luckily I always wear black trousers to work, but some crazy woman was wearing white. She stood up and had a very nasty-looking yellowish stain all over the seat of her trousers. I don't want to even start thinking about what was engrained in that seat.

Thursday 24 August

I watched a guy today pick his nose constantly while he was waiting for the train, and then with the same hand, proceeded to touch every single handle on the back of the seats as he walked to an available seat.

I'm amazed part of his brain didn't fall out as his finger was so far up there.

It was absolutely disgusting, and the look on my face said it all. He carried on having a good old rootle around when he sat down too. Gross.

This is the reason I refuse to touch any handle on any mode of public transport – the thought of encountering a dried-up bogey as I try to stay upright makes me want to retch.

And that is before I tell you about the bloke I saw on the Tube picking scabs off his head and holding onto the overhead hand rail.

Friday 25 August

Booked the day off. Result!

Monday 28 August

Bank holiday. Thank the Lord!

Tuesday 29 August

The trains are delayed due to over-running engineering works. Does this feel like a stuck record yet? Yes, it really bloody does. EVERY single time there is a bank holiday, the engineering works overrun. I am lost for words as to what to say quite frankly. Utterly, utterly useless.

Watching the departure time of my train get later and later, and the platform more and more crowded, I wonder for the umpteenth time, what the actual fuck I am doing with my life.

I arrive into work ninety minutes late, and my colleagues just look at me and shake their heads.

Wednesday 30 August

The days are starting to get shorter, but sadly my train journeys are not.

There is a thirty-minute delay again today due to a 'broken down freight train'. THAT old chestnut.

Why do freight trains run on the lines during rush hour? There must be a way of avoiding this.

I keep my eye out all the way to work for this bastard freight train, but there is not a sign of it.

It is almost like it is a made-up excuse for their general crapness. Surely that is not the case? Come on guys, think of something else for variation!

In goes another refund claim.

Thursday 31 August

There is a bloke crouching near the doorway on the train this evening smoking a joint. He thinks we cannot see him because he is scrunched into a ball, blowing smoke out a tiny hole in the space between carriages.

"FUCKING tell me not to smoke on trains," he bellows. "You fuckers."

I am only party to this because the train is yet again short formed and absolutely packed.

One brave soul tells him to put his joint out before the guard comes along.

"FUCK OFF!" he says. "Don't fucking tell me what to do."

The guard arrives, and joint guy proceeds to give him a good talking to - I've never heard quite so many profanities in one sentence before. I'm impressed. I make a mental note to use some of the more colourful ones myself in future.

I start feeling quite light-headed, as it is obviously some potent stuff, but we pull into a station and I see two police officers waiting by the door. I quickly wipe the stupid smile from my face.

They push their way on, grab the guy by the arms and march him out. He clings onto his joint as if his life depended on it.

The train manager gives a small shrug and then asks us to show him our tickets as we are crammed in the corridor with barely any room to move. I ask him if he seriously wants to see our tickets. He looks back at me totally deadpan. We all do a passable T-Rex impression trying to show him our tickets.

I hear a faint "You fuckers…" as we pull away from the platform. I know how you feel, mate.

SEPTEMBER

Friday 1 September

It definitely feels autumnal already – even though the mornings are still light(ish) and I'm getting home in the light. This is the last week of bloody kids on the train for a few weeks.

When one starts playing up or screeching like a banshee, in my head I repeat the mantra "*Back to school, back to school*" and smile to myself. However, I know the parents are thinking the same thing. Kudos to the teachers out there who give parents and commuters a much-needed break!

We had one kid on the journey back this evening, it had been to a matinee performance, and it decided to recap the songs it had heard during the musical.

While this may be deemed cute by some, the odd excerpt allows you to look up and smile at the cuteness. But this kid. THIS

KID. Decided to recite EVERY SONG IN FULL. And put it this way, it did not sound like the next Charlotte Church.

People had visibly wilted by the time I managed to leap off the train in sheer relief, and I think she had only reached the interval!

Monday 4 September

I decided to put a heavier coat on today as I felt a chill in the air. Big mistake. As soon as I arrived at the station, the weather became very mild all of a sudden, and for old time's sake, the heating was on in the carriage this morning too.

A guy had made the same mistake as me - he was toting a heavy-duty duffel coat on the platform. By the time we arrived in London he had stripped this off along with his jumper, his sleeves were rolled up to the max, too.

He resembled a Friesian cow thanks to the various sweat patches all over his shirt.

Tuesday 5 September

I switched back to my old light jacket today and it was BLOODY FREEZING. The air con was on full blast and I lost the feeling in my hands and feet about thirty minutes into my journey. To top it off, the weather decided to play along too and the temperature dropped several degrees for no reason.

I bought a jumper in my lunch break as I couldn't stand the cold any longer.

On the way back, you guessed it... the heating was set on Hades level and the carriage was sweltering. The train manager breezed through with a small smile on her face. She knew. SHE BLOODY KNEW.

Wednesday 6 September

The kids are back at school!! Praise be! The train platform was six deep again this morning as those parents who took time off to entertain their offspring over the summer return to work. The look of pleasure on their faces said it all! However, those of us without kids were rather miffed at having to compete for seats again. Time to sharpen the elbows.

Thursday 7 September

I always go for an 'airline' style seat if I can. Quite why they call it airline style is beyond me, it is infinitely more comfortable, with more leg room than you get on a plane – at least with my trains it is. Plus, some annoying twat in front cannot lean their chair right back and pin you to your seat which is what always happens when I take a flight.

However, there are rare times when I am forced to sit at a table. Today was one of them. The woman opposite was not happy, and she refused to move her legs over to her side of the table, instead challenging me to do something about it.

NEVER, EVER do that, my dear. I don't care how old you are, what position in a company you are, how 'important' you are – move your fucking feet to your own side.

I took great pleasure in standing on her feet as I got in the seat, and assumed the direct stare-into-the-eyes position. I was determined not to blink first. She huffed and puffed, she tutted and sighed, but eventually she moved her skinny, veiny legs back over to her side and broke eye contact.

Up yours, biyatch.

Friday 8 September

The trains were delayed today by another lorry strike - meaning yet another muppet driving an 18-wheeler had smacked straight into a railway bridge.

Unless a trucker possesses the same powers as the driver of the 'night bus' in *Harry Potter* who can squeeze through any gap, they really should deploy some common sense.

After an hour of hanging around the station waiting for a train to show up, I give up and go home. It was completely the right decision, because the trains didn't get back to normal until later this evening.

Monday 11 September

It is always a sad day as we remember the awful 9/11 bombings, and it makes you think that this type of thing could happen anywhere.

In a nice touch, the driver today asked us all to observe a minute's silence in honour of the victims. Everyone was happy to oblige.

A nice moment of solidarity for a change before we got back to our normal, moaning, miserable selves.

Tuesday 12 September

Watching two grown men fight over a seat is a pretty amusing pastime, and this morning we got a real treat. The train was short-formed (oh what a surprise – some blah about a fault in the 'original unit') so seats were at a minimum.

Luckily for me I hit the jackpot and was standing by the door when the train arrived, so I managed to get a seat fairly easily.

But these two blokes behind me had been jostling for a while and were both determined to get on at the same time.

One managed to push in front – and I mean push – by using his arms/elbows, and legged it to the only remaining spare seat. The losing guy tried to grab his coat and haul him back, but it was too late – he was beaten.

The losing bloke followed his competition to the seat and proceeded to call him a wanker and a rude, arrogant prick, for pushing him out of the way.

Seat guy just looked smug and kept his mouth shut.

The loser stood the whole journey right next to him, shaking his *Metro* in his face and generally getting in his personal space.

When we arrived in London, I watched them scuffle with each other out of the train and walk to the ticket barriers with an argument in full flow.

Wow. And these people actually have JOBS?!

Wednesday 13 September

The train was inexplicably late this evening – it was due, we had had nearly three days without an incident. Tonight, we just screeched to a halt in the middle of nowhere and waited. And waited and waited.

The train driver's voice came over the tannoy.

"Ladies and gentlemen. Sorry for this delay. This is your train driver. We are being held at a red signal for absolutely no reason. I can only apologise for us ruining your evening yet again. If it is any consolation, I'm supposed to be at a footie match with my mates this evening. I don't think that is going to happen."

He thought right.

After thirty minutes, we are informed that there has been a massive signal failure and it will take 'some time' to get through the huge tailback it has caused.

I glanced down at my iPod. The batteries were flat. F.U.C.K.

Thursday 14 September

I'm still smarting from the three-hour journey home last night. But I have a presentation this morning that I have to get in for.

I get up extra early to catch a 6am train. It is dark. It is cold. I stumble down the hill to my local station, and as soon as I turn the corner into the station, there is a sight that makes my heart sink.

There are train company staff in yellow jackets, surrounded by crowds of weary-looking commuters.

Trying not to start tearing great big chunks of my hair out, I wander up to earwig on what they are telling people.

Those bastard signals have all failed yet again. There are no trains for the foreseeable. Tickets will be accepted on other routes.

When asked how we access those other routes, we are met with a shrug and an "I don't know".

"But, but I've got a really important presentation this morning" I whimper.

Luckily, a nice man hears me and offers me a lift to the nearest station where trains from a rival company are running. I hug him

– even though it is not very professional. We make it to London in good time, with a few stares from the regular commuters who can recognise strangers in their midst; and I walk into my conference room sweating and hot. But I MADE it.

The presentation went really well you will be pleased to know, no thanks to my utterly useless, incompetent train company. Luckily the problem is resolved that day and the journey home actually goes according to plan. Miracles never cease.

Friday 15 September

Working from home today. After yesterday, I just cannot cope with the hassle.

Monday 18 September

I'm sitting there on the train minding my own business, when a guy asks if the seat next to me is free. I am nearly knocked out by the foul smell of extreme morning breath.

Jesus, what the hell does this man eat? The smell is a mix of stale fags, rotting meat, old potatoes and coffee.

"Certainly" I gasp, and move to let him in, feeling my stomach drop. The train is packed and there is nowhere but a cold luggage rack to sit in.

The fetid stench continues to waft at me for the next twenty minutes as he sits there breathing with his mouth open. WHY? Why sit there with your mouth open, panting like a fucking dog?

Eventually I can't stand it anymore, and feign a cramp in my leg. I tell a bloke standing near me that I need to stand up and he can have my seat.

He looks at me gratefully and sits down.

Two minutes later I see him recoil and look across at death breath with an incredulous look in his eye.

I can't help smiling. He looks round at me and catches me red-handed.

He knows I know.

Tuesday 19 September

It was fairly windy last night. And apparently a tree has blown down across the line just outside London.

Trains are running, but a) slowly (*Quelle surprise!*) and b) we risk being chucked out before we get to London to catch a Tube.

At least the option is there, we all agree. We all pile on as normal.

The train crawls along. It stops. It starts. It stops. It starts. Each stop and start is getting more jerky – I'm worried about whiplash.

Finally, we limp into the next station and are told to get out, they can't get us into London this morning, we have to get the next train back to our original station and 'await instructions'.

Because of a tree? Give me a fricking chainsaw and I'll cut the fucker up and out the way myself.

Stuff the instructions, I'm going home.

I think my boss actually cried when I told him I wouldn't be able to get into work today.

Wednesday 20 September – Friday 22 September

Three glorious days off and not once do I approach a train station. I revel in the bliss of getting in my car and driving where I want, when I want.

Monday 25 September

A couple were having train sex on the way home this evening -I kid you not.

Obviously it wasn't full blown 'how's your father', but they had a coat covering them and judging by the moans coming from the pair of them, it wasn't a peck on the cheek either.

He was wearing a fetching tracksuit and cap combo and she had on some dangerously tight jeans that allowed everything to spill out over the top with some hideous crop top on. Classy indeed.

This carried on for about half an hour and we were all feeling very uncomfortable – well apart from a dodgy-looking geezer three rows down, he looked like he was enjoying himself – ugh.

In the end, a more senior man in a pristine pinstripe suit turned around and said, "Do you MIND? Could you not wait until you get home? This is not acceptable behaviour at all."

The twat in the cap looked up, snarled in a very pleasant way and said, "Fuck off, old man".

Luckily the guard was coming down the aisle at this point as he had clocked them on the camera. They were ejected at the next station, where they were met by two rather large coppers.

It brought a whole new meaning to the phrase 'copping off'.

Tuesday 26 September

I received a massive thwack to my elbow this morning from the bloody refreshments trolley. It was that sodding woman again, the one who speeds down the aisles without giving anyone a chance to get out of the way.

This was all because I was leaning slightly outwards thanks to the selfish fucker next to me reading a copy of the *Wall Street Journal* at full spread.

Why would you do that? Fold the bloody thing, you selfish space-hogging asshole.

Why does any paper have to be so big in the first place? Has nobody taught the publishers that size isn't everything, and bigger is definitely not better? I resisted the urge to tear it in half.

I had to lean back in after that and took great pleasure in Mr Newspaper Dick having to read the rest of his news at a squashed angle. I hope his neck stayed like that all day.

He shook the paper out quite a few times, probably thinking it was a move of aggression to show his male dominance, but it just made him look like more of a prick than he already was.

Wednesday 27 September

The train was just pulling out of the station this evening when a guy started running alongside it, waving his hands and yelling for it to stop. He had apparently left his bag on the train and decided to go and get a coffee THREE MINUTES before it was due to leave. What a muppet! The coffee was all over the floor at this point and we could see a load of station staff running towards him. Someone asked him where his bag was and he pointed to a seat in our carriage with a bag on it.

In the quickest move I've ever seen, a guy on the train asks, "Is this anyone's bag?" – everyone shouts no, he grabs it, sprints to the door at the end of the carriage and throws the bag out of the window into his arms.

The man looks so relieved, even when he is pushed to the ground seconds later by three burly station security people leaping on his back.

The hero of the hour returns to his seat and a smattering of applause breaks out.

Coffee guy may have missed his train, and will probably be cautioned over his reckless behaviour, but he has got his stuff back. Small victories.

Thursday 28 September

A pair of doddery old tourists are waiting on the platform this morning with enough luggage to set up house somewhere else.

"Need any help with those, mate?" asks a regular.

"No thank you," the man replies prissily, "we can manage on our own."

"Suit yourself," he mutters.

The train pulls up and typically the door stops right where they are. It is one of the 'newer', automatic door trains this morning that give you no second chance to get on. We all surge forward when the door opens, but the old codger is having none of it.

He picks up his cases one by one and takes each one onto the train, fussing around the luggage rack until they are just so.

The guard starts to blow the whistle and we are still waiting to get on.

"MOVE," urges one person.

"HURRY UP," urges another.

Still the old fart is taking his time, and the old dragon with him is standing in the doorway blocking it.

"GET ON THE TRAIN," bellows the guard.

Suddenly a bloke next to me breaks. He physically pushes the woman on the train, grabs their last two bags, flings them into the carriage and we all pile on in a rush as the doors start to close.

"You stupid old git" someone said as they went past. He is not amused and starts muttering to himself.

They get to their seats, and he insists on sitting by the window. For the rest of the journey, he is up and down to the toilet, making his companion move every time and thoroughly pissing off the other people sitting at their table. I'm not normally a fan of euthanasia, but…

Friday 30 September

What better way to end the month than with a day off and a long weekend?

OCTOBER

Monday 2 October

I woke up to the most wonderful fog today – not only is it pitch black in the mornings again already, but it is sodding raining as well – I had a sinking feeling as the trees were shedding their leaves at a rate of knots over the weekend. I trudged down to the station in wind, rain and fog (what a delightful combo) and, sure enough, there were crowds of people milling around all over the place.

As usual, not a single station staff member was anywhere to be seen, the blinds at the 'service desks' were pulled down and I could swear I saw shadows moving behind them as they cowered there away from the increasingly agitated bunch of commuters.

I fought my way up to the platform to get some space, and it was absolutely rammed up there too – not a good sign.

Luckily for us, the hapless Twitter team were on hand with an explanation. There had been massive 'leaf fallage' further up the track, which was causing the trains to slip when braking.

I genuinely didn't believe that leaves on the line were actually a thing, but for the first time in sixteen years, it has been used as a legitimate excuse.

Seriously? A few fricking leaves? No wonder the staff were hiding, I felt mad enough to go all Basil Fawlty with a branch and some choice swear words.

I decided to go home rather than hang around wet commuters all morning. I explained to my boss why the trains weren't running and he just sighed and muttered "whatever".

Tuesday 3 October

Luckily for me, someone had got hold of a broom from somewhere overnight and managed to sweep the pesky leaves out of the way so the trains could run without slipping. This problem caused the trains to run late all day yesterday.

I wonder if they had a fancy title like

'track leaf coordinator' or 'cross-network foliage manager'?

Wednesday 4 October

I was sitting there, minding my own business when the guy in the seat across from me starts sneezing violently. After the fifth sneeze, I glance over and see that the dirty bastard is not covering his nose or his face and is just sneezing with his vile maw gaping wide, scattering his germs far and wide.

The woman next to him, who is pinned in the window seat, is sitting there with a look of absolute horror on her face and she has buried her chin in the collar of her shirt.

"AaaaaaitCHOOOOOOOO!" he goes again, but this time he wipes his hands on the seat in front of him. I can feel the germ-filled droplets landing on my face.

After the third in this particular set, and I can see a bald guy two rows ahead wiping his dome, I've just about had enough.

"Excuse me," I say to snot man, "would you like a tissue?"

I am holding one aloft like some kind of banner.

"Oh no thanks, I don't need one" he says, sniffing back some mucus.

"I think you do" I reply and drop the tissue in his lap.

The woman next to him looks at me gratefully from over her Harry Hill collar.

I await the next sneeze with anticipation. It doesn't come. But I have a feeling he has infected a few people with his vile germs.

Thursday 5 October

I was eternally grateful to wake up with no hint of a cold this morning. My vicious scrubbing of hands, face, neck, *inside* my nose and gargling of antiseptic when I arrived in my office, had obviously warded off any germs that were flying around yesterday. I had even washed my hair last night in case the germs tried to permeate my skull through my hair follicles.

Before commuting I never had paranoia quite so badly, but my phobia of germs increases each week as I continue to see a lack of basic personal hygiene standards among some of my fellow travellers.

On the way to work this morning I jump of out my seat when a guy behind me starts sneezing. Luckily he had a gigantic handkerchief and was sneezing away into that.

Now hankies are another subject entirely – they are either soggy or crispy – why are people so averse to tissues around here?

Do they know something I don't?

Friday 6 October

I wake up with a stinking cold. So much for my smug I-beat-the-odds attitude yesterday. Fuck face got me.

If I saw him now, I would ram a whole box of tissues up each nostril as a reminder.

Eyes streaming, and sneezing like one of the seven dwarves, I decide to work from home so I don't pass it onto everyone I come into contact with.

If only fuck face had done that on Wednesday, I'd be breathing easy and sat in my office quite happily.

Monday 9 October

My cold has now progressed to an annoying cough. I feel like I am rattling around with the amount of Day/Night Nurse pills I am popping.

I drag my sorry behind to the station this morning, and get on the train. Then it begins. That tickle in the throat that will only go away if you cough.

I grope around for my water bottle and find just a few drops of stale water left in the bottom. I have forgotten to fill it up. SHIT.

Give a quick cough and the relief is instant.

After about fifteen minutes, this is happening at minute intervals. The cough is getting on everybody's nerves, it is getting on mine the most, but there is nothing I can do.

A woman turns around and glares at me. Then a bloke does the same thing. Someone else jams in their headphones.

Where is the fricking refreshment trolley when you need it?

Eyes streaming and throat aching from the coughing, I see the shape of the 'on-board customer retail host' making his way down the neighbouring carriage.

He eventually gets to me.

"Have you got any water please?" I gasp.

"Sorry," he trills, "I sold the last bottle a few minutes ago."

I am forced to buy a fucking Fruit Shoot thing for nearly £3.

Now I have the alternate pleasure of coughing and then gagging as I try to imbibe a sugar-filled 'drink' to keep my throat lubricated.

To top it off, the drink turns my tongue purple. My boss kindly pointed that out in our first meeting of the day. The dye lasts for HOURS.

Tuesday 10 October

I was sent home from work early today because my cough was doing everyone's head in.

I'm armed with cough medicine, water and even cough drops, but nothing stops me once a coughing fit takes hold.

I sit in a relatively empty carriage and hope for the best.

In the middle of one bout, I hear a bloke mutter "Oh, For God's SAKE" before getting up with all his 'look-at-me-I'm-important' gear trailing behind him and moving to another carriage.

I'm quite tempted to follow him and sit in the other carriage, just to see what he does.

Wednesday 11 October

I spent the day at home coughing my lungs up.

Thursday 12 October

My cough is now under control enough for me to venture back to the station. Luckily, it is a bright and crisp morning, which does wonders for my lungs.

I spot the miserable sod who moved carriages on the platform ahead and deliberately go and stand right next to him. I issue a gentle cough.

His head snaps round, his eyes widen as he clocks who I am.

He picks up his stuff and heads down the platform to the waiting room – a classic tactic for avoiding someone, as it means you can emerge just before the train arrives and stand in a completely different place.

I've done it myself a couple of times on the pretence that it was too cold to stand outside. Unfortunately for me, the people I was trying to avoid actually followed me.

I felt I had tortured the man enough, so I reluctantly let him go. But his face is in my memory now. His cards are marked!

Friday 13 October

Some people will not travel on Friday the 13th. But I figured being a commuter, it couldn't get much worse than it already was.

The trains were wonderfully empty today and shockingly they were on time.

On the way home, I was not so lucky, as it was packed with casual travellers and their suitcases. *"Why so many suitcases?"* I wondered.

Then it hit me. It was half-term next week. Oh bollocks.

Monday 16 October

Half-term week starts like this.

Platform 2, 7.49am.

"DADDY, IS THE TRAIN COMING NOW?" yells an angelic-looking child.

"No, darling, it will be here in a few minutes" whispers the father, clearly a commuter taking his son out for the day.

"WHEN IS IT COMING, DADDY?" shouts the child five seconds later.

"Soon, darling, now keep your voice down, you don't want to annoy everybody else."

"WHY AM I ANNOYING EVERY-BODY ELSE?"

Father just sighs and looks down at the ground. His partner who is standing there with a sleeping baby in her arms, just smiles and leaves him to it.

They get on the same carriage as me.

"DADDY, HOW LONG UNTIL WE ARE IN LONDON?"

I watch the people already in the carriage recoil as they realise this child is with them ALL the way. But it is amusing me greatly.

"Shhhh, son, we will be there in about an hour, you have to stay very quiet or the conductor lady will tell you off."

"WHY WILL SHE TELL ME OFF? I HAVEN'T DONE ANYTHING DADDY".

Silence. A tablet comes out and quiet descends.

Half an hour later, I glance over and the harassed-looking father has dozed off, hoping repeat episodes of *Paw Patrol* will do the trick.

Seconds later, he is snapped awake so abruptly he must have given himself whiplash.

"DADDY. DADDY. DADDEEEEEEEEE, DADDEEEEEEEE – ARE WE IN LONDON

YET? I'M BOOOORREEEED. I NEED A POO."

I am trying frantically not to laugh at this point. Nobody else seems to find it funny, but for some reason I think of this little lad who is excited to be spending time with his dad and coming to London as well, and it just tickles me. The baby remains sleeping the whole journey and the mum looks fairly serene. She drew the best hand this time and she knows it. Well done, lady! Nicely played!

He quietens down for a while, but as we get off the train in London I hear him shriek in the distance, "DADDY, DADDY, DADDY, WHERE ARE WE GOING NOW?"

The guy is in for a very long day. Something tells me he will be glad to get back to work for a rest.

Tuesday 17 October

The train is full of families again this morning. I have to wade my way through empty sandwich boxes, crisp packets, sweet wrappers and God knows what, just to get to a seat. I pity the cleaner this evening.

By 6pm, they will be lucky if they can actually find the pathway between the seats amid all the rubbish people are chucking all over the place. They may need a snorkel and fins to get around.

"Do they live like this at home?" I wonder. Dirty bastards.

Wednesday 18 October

I catch an early train today as I've got to head over to Paris on the Eurostar.

I head to the Eurostar terminal and am confronted with crowds of people milling about.

Just for a fucking change, the trains are running late. I'm glad I have a booked seat.

When we finally get on, I wish my company had the decency to pay for first class seats.

The legroom is non-existent and I have a box thing in front of my legs that holds brochures etc. Who actually reads that shit? Just give me more leg room.

The ride over is actually fairly quick, but when we get to France, one of the first stops sees a load of dodgy-looking people get on who are clearly doing a recce of the carriage.

Sure enough, it turns out that five people had their laptops stolen at the next station

– they had got up to go to the loo, thinking they were safe, but the thieves are practiced hands, and swiped their possessions as soon as their backs were turned.

Never, ever leave anything unattended. It just isn't worth the hassle.

The journey back is smooth, and for once in my life I make the connection to my homeward-bound train with no problems. Boy, am I going to suffer for that one day!

Thursday 19 October

I'm working from home today as it was a long day yesterday. Because I live near the railway line I can see them going past. Hardly any went past today - I felt I had dodged a bullet when it came on the news that some scumbag had, yet again, stolen the copper wiring from the overhead lines and the trains had ground to a complete halt.

Twitter went absolutely mad. People saying they had booked shows for half-term, were supposed to be catching flights etc.

They got the usual response, "We are sorry for any inconvenience caused."

Inconvenience? It is more than a fucking inconvenience, it actually ruins people's days. That person going for a job interview. That person going for promotion. That person whose first week it is in the office. The person whose early meeting could set them up with a commission that will keep them going the whole year. The families planning trips they have saved up for. I could go on.

I hope the selfish bastards who did this electrocute themselves. Karma would be a great thing.

But don't call any delay an 'inconvenience'. It is far more than that.

How about I wrap the tannoy microphone round your head? Would that be an 'inconvenience' too?

Friday 20 October

I check the Trainline site and check Twitter. Reams of people are complaining about how they were stranded last night thanks to emergency engineering works.

Risk a train today? Nope. Screw that, I'm staying right where I am.

Monday 23 October

On the way home tonight, a man gets on the

train with a full-blown leather office chair. Seriously. It is a giant of a chair. I'm quite jealous. He parks it in the vestibule area and just sits there on it like he is some kind of god.

There is a hairy moment when Jobsie the train manager comes down and asks him what he is doing with a chair on the train, and he cockily replies, "Sitting on it".

He gets a round of applause for that one.

Jobsie tells him the train is no place for a chair, and that he has to get off at the next station.

"S'OK, that's where I'm going" replies the bloke.

Jobsie is now in a foul mood as there is nothing he can do. He makes us all get our tickets out and scrutinises them more than ever, just hoping for a little error so he can feel better about himself by finding someone to pick on.

He finds nothing.

Sweeeeet! Sorry, not sorry, Jobsie.

Tuesday 24 October

The trains are running late again because of leaves on the line. Surely they all fell the other week? Judging by how late the train was before, there can't be many more leaves left?

I actually thought the station manager was joking, because no train company really gets affected by leaves twice in one month, does it?

He wasn't joking. His poker face said it all. The second leaf fall of the month meant we were yet again running late.

My suggestion of 'sticking a brush to the first train of the day' and brushing the leaves out the way were greeted with stony silence.

"It is not that simple madam" was all he said.

I beg to differ, sunshine.

Wednesday 25 October

Today, ladies and gentlemen, we have a hen party from Derby on board. How did I know that? Probably because they kept shouting "DERBY HENS" and clinking their fruit-flavoured cider cans together.

There are about ten of them, spread across a couple of tables and the odd seat. One bloke next to one of the women is hunched down with headphones on with his eyes clamped tightly shut.

"DO YOU WANT ANOTHER CIDER, DOREEN?" bellows one.

"EEEEH – GO ON THEN" bellows Doreen.

We are then treated to a bit of a singsong – God know what they are singing – some northern ditty I think, and loudly discussing how they are going to get "absolutely bladdered" today.

One is wearing a veil and she has long blonde hair. How nice that she has her mum and all her aunts and older relatives with her on her hen weekend, I think.

Then she turns around.

Jesus. It is a lights-on-in-the-nightclub moment. She has a face resembling an aged prune, and she is missing a few teeth.

"I'M OFF T'BOG," she announces to her assembled hens.

"WAHEEEEEEEEY," they all scream.

I turn my headphones to full volume and close my eyes, hoping it will all go away. It doesn't.

I can only imagine the absolute hunk she will be marrying and how beautiful the wedding pictures will be.

Thursday 26 October

Just when I think I couldn't encounter a worse person than the bride of Frankenstein yesterday, there is a woman on the train this evening who decides to clip her fingernails in full view of everyone.

Out come the clippers, and we are all treated to 'clip' sounds for the next five minutes as she sends fragments of nail in all directions.

The look of horror on people's faces is actually quite amusing, but I cannot believe the brass neck of the woman.

She then starts filing away, blowing nail dust into the atmosphere.

I half expected her to start on her toenails, but thankfully she doesn't.

Friday 27 October

There must be some sort of charity bike ride going on this weekend. The platform was full of cyclists this morning – mainly middle-aged men with paunches wearing Lycra and wheeling £2,000+ bikes as if they have a clue what they are doing.

One guy decides to show off and does that one foot in the pedal thing, using the other to propel him along. Unfortunately, when it came to stopping, he couldn't get his foot out the clip, and ended up crashing into one of his saggy-bottomed friends.

He did get a loud "Waheeeeey" from a few regular commuters though. Who's to say we don't revel in other people's misery?

Monday 30 October

A bloke gets on the train in London today, and for some unbeknown reason decides to stand, even though there are plenty of empty seats.

As the train pulls off, the guard comes past and tells him there are plenty of seats all over the train.

"I'd rather stand" he replies.

"But the trolley is going to be coming down the aisles soon" says the guard.

"I'll move then" he says.

However, when the trolley actually arrives, he barely moves at all, forcing the on-board retail host to squeeze past him at a very awkward angle and banging some poor woman on the knee as she goes past.

The woman glares at the bloke standing up, but he really doesn't give a tin shit and just keeps reading his book.

Tuesday 31 October

Happy Halloween, folks. The train staff are giving away orange-iced cupcakes at the station this morning, and the driver makes a few ghost noises when announcing which stations we are all calling at. It certainly puts us in a good mood for the morning.

However, the ghouls take over in the evening, and the train is delayed due to... INSERT ANSWER HERE...

Yep, broken down freight train. We crawl along. We stop. We crawl, we stop. We wait. Repeat *ad infinitum.*

The good mood established this morning with the cupcakes has now gone and everyone is in their usual huffy puffy mood. Funnily enough, there were no cupcakes on offer this evening.

Two and a half hours later, I get home.

If any trick or treaters knock on my door tonight, they will regret it.

NOVEMBER

Wednesday | November

I dragged my sorry behind to the station this morning, and amazingly the trains were running.

It must still be Halloween, because I saw an apparition on the train that I couldn't believe was real.

A guy was sitting at one of the tables (wearing a suit) and talking to his mate. But at the same time, he was flossing his teeth.

YES. FLOSSING HIS TEETH.

What the actual fuck is going on? Clipping nails is one thing, but who actually flosses their teeth on a train?

He wasn't just gently pulling floss in and out of his teeth either, he was flicking it. I'm just glad I wasn't sitting opposite him.

His mate didn't seem at all bothered by the dirty bastard he was hanging around with. Nor did he seem to think his friend was doing anything out of the ordinary, as they were talking about garage doors. Seriously?

The flossing went on for about twenty minutes – he must have eaten some stringy shit that morning.

People are absolutely dumbfounded at this sight and some are staring at him with their mouths open.

"I wouldn't do that" I thought to myself, clamping my own teeth shut.

He finishes flossing, sprays some breath spray and then drops his plaque-filled floss on the floor where it lies like some putrid, yellow-flecked micro-worm.

I am left speechless.

You dirty fucking bastard.

Thursday 2 November

Today is one of the most disturbing days in my year. The day I renew my season ticket. The guy behind the glass window says "That will be £8,200 please."

"No, I don't want first class," I say, "just a standard ticket, no Tube."

"Yep, £8,200" he says.

I hand over my credit card – I'm lucky

I'm on a company scheme where I pay the loan back interest free over 12 months.

Let me break that down. That is more than my mortgage, the price of a basic new car, and several luxury holidays.

That one piece of paper I am now in possession of is more valuable than anything else I carry or drive.

And what do I get for this amount of money? No guaranteed seat, no guaranteed service, treated like absolute shit on a daily basis, and the only thing guaranteed is that the price will just keep rising.

I say a quick thanks to Maggie Thatcher and all the bloody useless governments since that have failed to do anything to stop our train network ripping passengers off and making ours the most expensive system in Europe.

And by thanks, read a two-fingered mental salute.

Friday 3 November

I am still sulking about my season ticket. I hate everyone, everything, and most of all trains and the greedy corporate bastards who decide the rip-off ticket prices. Oh, and fuck the shareholders too.

Monday 6 November

Despite Bonfire Night officially taking place yesterday, we were still treated to a number of over-the-top displays during our journey home this evening.

Obviously people had forgotten how to use a calendar, or had bought a job lot of cheap fireworks from a discount store and needed to use them up.

Two stops from home, a group of 'yoofs' get on with their hoodies and their big-man 'street' accents and start threatening everyone in the carriage that they will let off some fireworks inside. They are waving what we can only assume are fireworks in their grubby little hands.

Most of us are so knackered we can barely react, but one older gentleman near the door scurries out to get the train manager. He doesn't come back – what a wuss.

Next thing, Jobsie turns up. He makes a call on his walkie-talkie as the yoofs jeer at him, and as the train pulls into the next station there is a bit of a scuffle as two British Transport Police officers walk in the opposite end.

The yoofs push past Jobsie as if to make

an escape at the other end of the carriage, but two more police officers are already waiting.

We watch in smug satisfaction as they drag the little scrotes away with them along the platform and into a waiting squad car. Part of me hopes they light the fireworks and stick them down their pathetic, baggy, grey tracksuit bottoms. Kudos to Jobsie though, he stuck it to them.

Tuesday 7 November

We are entertained today by a table of American tourists – clearly who have not been to London before – talking about all the sights they are going to see.

One of them is called Blanche. My day is officially made. Blanche is obviously feeling jetlagged, because Blanche does not really want to talk that much.

So her friend shouting, "What do you think Blanche? BLANCHE?" every five minutes is probably going to seriously irritate her after a while.

We endure about ten shouted Blanches before the train pulls into London and it is then that Blanche springs to life.

"WE ARE HERE" she yells, bolting

out the door and sprinting to the ticket barriers.

Unfortunately for her she is fazed by the ticket barriers themselves, "IT'S NOT WORKING, IT'S NOT WORKING!!" she screams at the station staff, pushing frantically at the black rubber gates.

It turns out that she is trying to insert the entire plastic folder that encircles her train ticket, rather than the ticket itself.

Bless. If they use the underground, poor Blanche could be in for a difficult day.

Wednesday 8 November

Two smooth journeys today. I have nothing to complain about. Nothing beats leaving when you are supposed to and arriving when you are supposed to.

Thursday 9 November

It is officially black tie season in London now. As I'm waiting to board my train this evening, there is a group of about twelve, sixty-something blokes in black tie stomping their way down the platform. They have obviously had a bit of a tipple on the train on the way down. One ricochets off a woman dragging a suitcase, causing her to stumble and fall into the bloke in front.

Both turn around and glare at said penguin-suited bloke, but he is beyond caring. His large, red nose shows he is obviously a seasoned pro at this drinking game, but perhaps not so seasoned at walking in a straight line.

His friends, who have all obviously been drinking too, start shouting, "Come on old boy", "Steady now, chap" and equally ridiculous sayings, as they crash their way through the barriers.

The growing crowd of us waiting on the platform watch their progress down the station as they all attempt to link arms and walk along.

It came a bit unstuck when – after pushing past a number of disgruntled travellers – they got to the escalator, and realised that only one would fit on at a time.

Friday 10 November

The train was particularly crowded this morning. I ended up stuck behind a Japanese girl who was about the size of a six-year-old child. She was absolutely terrified of the escalator and every time a step came towards her she put her foot on it and jerked it off again.

She also had a gigantic wheelie case (of course she bloody did), and she tried a different tactic of putting that on first, watching it move and then trying to step on after that. Nobody could get past her.

It was quite amusing at first – don't they have escalators in Japan???- but after about ten attempts, people behind me were starting to get impatient and were beginning to push. It was becoming a life-threatening situation here.

I tapped her on the shoulder and pointed to the lift – she spoke absolutely no English – marvellous.

Eventually after my increasingly frantic gestures, she gets it, realises she is in a packed station, looks behind her and just runs off with a horrified look on her face, dragging her mammoth case behind her.

I launch myself down the escalator before I am pushed down them by the wall of people tutting and swearing behind me. Welcome to London, tourists! The home of the tolerant.

Monday 13 November

I have a random day off today and intend to stay fully away from the trains.

Tuesday 14 November

It is really bloody cold this morning. There has been a huge frost and I can feel my feet sticking to the ground as I walk to the station.

Obviously it is too cold for the trains as well. The tracks have frozen and are too cold for trains to travel on them at any speed.

I mean, seriously? OK, it is about minus ten degrees today (well it feels like it), but too cold for supposedly strong steel tracks to run trains on?

Pull the other one. What I really think has happened is that somebody couldn't be arsed to get out of bed this morning, and as a result, the trains were all running late.

I'm not bitter, but I hope they develop bed sores, the lazy bastards.

Wednesday 15 November

There was a bit of an incident in London today. A minute before the train is due to leave, a middle-aged businessman runs along the platform shouting "WAIT, PLEASE LET ME ON" at the top of his voice as the guard whistle sounds and the doors lock. The conductor is shouting back, "GET AWAY FROM THE TRAIN."

The man tries to open the door and his hand is slapped away by the conductor. The man then lobs the cup of whatever he is drinking at the conductor and scores a bullseye. Right in the face. It is Jobsie. Oh shit.

Jobsie unlocks the doors and gets out. The man tries to get on. Some pushing and shouting ensues. We are all pressed up against the window watching. Who cares if we are late home today? This is class. It almost makes the season ticket price worth it.

Several platform staff run to restrain the guy who is screaming 'WANKER' at the top of his voice. The police arrive. The man is dragged off down the platform, still screaming 'WANKER'.

Everyone returns to their seats and opens their books/turns on various devices. It is as if nothing has happened.

Thursday 16 November

Why do some train managers feel compelled to fill the blissful silence of a commuter train with their utter garbage about tickets?

We have one particular guy who will not stop talking in his monotone voice – explaining every stop along the way, and then launching into the different ticket types.

"If you purchase a super-easy-peasy off peak, you can only catch the 19.35, 20.00 (and every single train after). If you have a travelcard from so and so, you can only travel on…etc, etc…but if you don't have the right ticket you will be required to buy a new one at full price.."

You get the gist. By the time I get home an hour later, he has just finished talking.

As I close the door, I hear his dulcet tones start up again:

"Welcome to the 20.15 train, I'd just like to run through some ticket information…"

AAARRGGGH!! SHUT UP, MAN. JUST SHUT UP.

Friday 17 November

A woman sits next to me today on the train home and falls asleep.

Her mouth is open extremely wide and she is snoring.

That is all good – I have headphones. I don't care.

However, her head suddenly lolls onto my shoulder and she sits there with dribble hanging from her lips.

I am horrified! I can't bear physical contact with another person on the train and I don't want a wet patch on my coat – that is disgusting.

I shrug my shoulder she is leaning on quite roughly, once, twice... and she suddenly jerks away and bangs her head on the window with a rather large thud.

She is most definitely not asleep now.

The only problem is that she is glaring at me like I was the one who smacked her head against the window. If she carries on looking at me like that, I might give her a second experience.

Happy Friday everyone!

Monday 20 November

For some reason the platform is absolutely packed this morning.

There are no delays, everything is running smoothly, or so it seems.

Then the train arrives. It is five carriages. AGAIN. Two of them are first class.

Turns out the previous two trains have been short as well, all because of a line-side fire somewhere further up north that has blocked the tracks.

The train is packed. But we squeeze on with a lot of pushing and shoving. My head is rammed up against a vestibule wall and I am surrounded by people still wearing their rucksacks on their shoulders.

After the third or fourth time of some cornered-thing poking into my neck, I ask the guy next to me if he would mind putting his rucksack on the floor as it was poking into me.

He looks at me incredulously for a second, before shifting it to his other shoulder.

It immediately pokes a smartly dressed man in the back of the head.

I settle in and wait for the drama to unfold as the smart man's face gets redder and redder. By the end of the journey, the rucksack is on the floor.

Monday 22 November

Well, what a surprise! The trains still aren't

back to normal after last week's performance, so we are stuck with another short-formed train this morning.

However, this time I have my elbows at the ready and I push my way on, make a beeline for one of the handful of empty seats, and sit down.

I chose wisely. Two minutes later, some annoying git with a Barbour jacket on, comes over to the bloke who sat in the next row and did the old "Excuse me, this is my seat" scenario.

The bloke refuses to move, explaining that this was not a normal service. An argument ensues, with the two guys trading increasingly rude insults to each other about their appearance, their guts (or lack of), their hair, until the other one just screams, "GET OUT OF MY SEAT."

He doesn't, and I watch the defeated guy push his way past all the people crammed in the aisles – so much tutting and "For FUCK's sakes" being muttered. Possibly he's hoping to find a conductor.

He never returns. Damn, just as the entertainment was starting to get good!

Tuesday 23 November

Every morning as the train pulls into London, the on-board customer retail host goes up and down the carriages bearing a large green sack, shouting, "RUBBISH, ANY RUBBISH" at the top of her voice.

She gives no fucks that people are asleep or are hoping to gently wake out of their slumber as they reach their destination. If they don't hear her and have a cup in front of them, rather than just putting it in the sack herself, she shouts "RUBBISH, ANY RUBBISH" right in their ear.

I do find it pretty amusing to watch them snap awake and fumble for their empty cup or biscuit wrapper.

What is not so funny is that the bags are all piled up by the door. There has been many a time I have nearly caught my foot in a bag and gone tumbling out the door.

One woman did this morning, but she fell onto the back of the man in front of her, and he gave her an impromptu piggy-back along the platform.

They were both red-faced, but it earned them a cheer at least! Who knows, it could have been the start of a beautiful relationship.

Wednesday 24 November

I sat next to an animal this evening. Actually that is unfair. Animals are civilised creatures.

He had a giant plastic bag full of food. He started eating with his lips champing together, gulping like a bullfrog at dusk, and then chucking all his crap all over the joint. Sandwich boxes, napkins, sweet wrappers – they all went onto the floor.

By the time we arrived at my station, we were neck deep in detritus and I had to virtually swim out of my seat.

Friday 25 November

I was early on the train this evening and my eye wandered over to a woman watching something on her tablet. Being nosy, I strained to see what it was, as I could hear tinny voices. This particular woman was watching a mattress advert at full volume. I thought it must just be an ad break, but when I glanced over about twenty minutes later, the same advert was on a loop and she was staring at it transfixed.

OK. I wonder if she realises there are actual programmes that you can download that are pretty interesting and informative, or perhaps she just has a mattress fetish. Did someone say box spring?

Monday 27 November

A youngish woman gets on the train this morning at the stop after me and she is clearly into whatever is on her iPod. She is lip-synching like a boss after five minutes. Then the power grabs start, and she goes into full-on ballad mode. All of this is perfectly silent, but her eyes are clamped shut and she must truly believe nobody can see her.

We are all watching slack-jawed as she mimes her way through a four-minute song. I think it was Jennifer Rush, but I'm not sure. When she finishes, she opens her eyes and realises we are all staring in amazement. Someone gives her a clap.

Her face turns so red that I feel sorry for her, but secretly hope we get another performance.

We don't. Her miming days are over. But she was certainly more in time than Cheryl Cole could ever hope to be.

Tuesday 28 November

A packed train home, no seats (GRRRR), so I'm standing in my favourite vestibule along with a bunch of other pissed-off looking people. Some bloody annoying woman decided to stand there waving her frothy coffee all over the place as she showed off on her phone and talked her unfortunate friend on the other end through a 'fantastic' job interview she had today.

The train lurched and yep, you, guessed it, the coffee went all over me – somehow, she had managed to arc it so it went behind her and it went all over my black trousers.

"Oh, I'm so sorry" she gasped. Then she turned away and carried on talking to her friend with no offer of getting a tissue, while I stood there dripping foamy coffee like some freaky Mr Darcy striding out of the pond in *Pride and Prejudice*.

Wednesday 29 November

In a very amusing move, I volunteered for the passenger council last month, and it was the first meeting tonight. All I had to do was attend two meetings, and I qualified for four free train tickets for friends and family. Easy peasy.

I turned up with my long list of 'issues', only to be told that the agenda had already been decided six months beforehand, and we were not straying.

We listened to a fucking boring old fart (actually a commuter) called Cecil, wittering on about different types of trains, and then had to listen to a presentation by the train operator's technical guy about Wi-Fi on board trains.

When asked if we had any questions, I asked how they justified the huge fare prices, and why the service was consistently unreliable, but apparently my questions were not in keeping with the meeting.

Cecil (and trust me, if I see him around he will get a black eye) tells me in his nasal voice that those questions are "inappropriate" for this meeting, and to "please stick to the agenda".

He then nearly wet his pants when the train company staff produced samples of next year's first-class food menu.

I made my excuses and left pretty quickly after that. Sorry friends and family. You will have to buy your own sodding tickets.

Thursday 30 November

A lady gets on our train this morning with a blackbird on one shoulder, a cat on the other and a small dog in her arms.

She proceeds to sit down like everything is perfectly normal, while we all gape at her.

Not one of those animals moved or made a sound. They just blinked at each other and at the woman.

Someone gets their phone out to take a picture, and she says, "Please don't do that. We hate having our picture taken." The phone duly disappears.

She gets off at the stop before London, and everybody is just left speechless.

We are all pissed off that none of us could take pictures and put them up on Facebook. Who would believe us otherwise?

DECEMBER

Friday 1 December

I am feeling decidedly Christmassy. Lights and trees are starting to appear everywhere and I feel like I'm getting in the Christmas spirit. Then the train is delayed on the way home due to our old friend – the classic signal failure. My Christmassy mood evaporates and I sit there seething the whole way home, until three hours later I actually walk through my front door. Another Friday evening ruined by trains. FFS. I reach for the gin. Repeat.

Monday 4 December

We had our first drunk fight of the season on this very train. Although to be fair, I don't think it mattered to these two individuals what time of year it was. She was shouting through her three remaining teeth at her baseball be-capped, tracksuit-clad companion to just "eff the eff off you wanker" and pushing him around, and he replied through his mouthful of two blackened teeth, "No, you eff the eff off, you ugly effing bitch" and pushed her back.

Neither spilled their Special Brew though, despite a few hefty pushes back and forth. When it came to my stop, I just said "Excuse me" and walked right through them.

He said "Oh, sorry" and moved out of the way. As soon as I had gone through, they started shouting and pushing each other again.

Tuesday 5 December

There was a delightful guy on the train this evening. Drunk as a skunk, wearing faded dirty jeans, with his belly hanging below the bottom of his T-shirt and sat with his equally drunk mates. As our journey progressed, I kept smelling beef crisps and thought one of them was eating a packet. You can tell Christmas is round the corner! Then we start hearing long, loud belches, and the beef smell gets stronger.

At the first stop, he comes up the carriage, and as he passes me, he emits the longest belch I have ever heard, leaving a delightful mix of beer and beef crisp fumes in his wake. It makes me physically gag.

We can still hear him as he gets off the train, belching his way along the platform like some vile beef crisp-breath-fuelled steam engine.

Wednesday 6 December

The alcohol-induced fun continued tonight – a youngish woman, who had clearly had a couple of bevvies during the day, decides to start singing along to her iTunes at the top of her voice.

Well, it sounded like a cat being strangled, but everyone was so amused that we let her carry on. Mariah Carey had actually never sounded so good to me!

The amusement soon wore off when she went through the song for the seventh time though.

By the time I got off the train, all I wanted for Christmas was earplugs!

Thursday 7 December

We were all just sitting there quietly this morning - it must be the time of year when nobody has any energy left - when a guy in our carriage gave off a huge snort and then woke himself up shouting "YES" at the top of his voice.

The whole carriage just started laughing – the look on his face was priceless. He was pretty embarrassed, but took it in good humour.

Friday 8 December

Another day off today – I'm trying to use up that holiday. I decided to get on a train headed north. I thought I'd get some money off my ticket, being a season ticket holder.

Turns out I don't. Screw you then.

The train ran according to time going north, but soon as it headed south, the mysterious broken-down train appeared again, although nobody ever saw it. Is there a train Bermuda triangle on my line? One that only appears every now and again, and only when I actually want to get home!

Monday 11 December

Worst nightmare – I have lost my season ticket. I discovered it had disappeared on my way home from London when Jobsie decided to check everyone's tickets.

I must have dropped it when I rushed through the barrier and not put it back in my holder properly. I felt like a criminal.

I had to pay for a full-price ticket (three figures) and arrange for another ticket in the morning so I can get a refund. Luckily, I still have my photo ID card – so it shouldn't be too bad.

Tuesday 12 December

I felt like a schoolchild. I was scolded for losing my ticket and told that if I lose it again, I will have to pay the full price. Erm – excuse me?

He made me fill in a form for my refund. The form demanded my name, weight, religion, preferred sexual position and asked if I had a first-born, would I consider giving them up in return for a new season ticket.

Eventually the guy behind the counter was satisfied and issued me with a new ticket. When I asked when I'd get my money back for the other ticket, he replied, "Should be before Christmas, but it is a busy time of year".

I resisted the urge to call him a sanctimonious git as I flounced off.

Wednesday 13 December

So perhaps I was a little merry this evening after a few pre-Christmas drinks with my workmates this afternoon.

I smiled at everyone as I walked up the carriage – got some funny looks in return as I normally look like I'm chewing a wasp, then fell fast asleep and missed my sodding stop.

I had to go one further and come back. I actually found it funny. Not sure the other passengers found my laughing to myself amusing, particularly as I sounded like Barbara Windsor on steroids.

Thursday 14 December

I had a hangover all day. I just started to feel human as I boarded the train home. Who should sit next to me? A ridiculously drunken woman. She sat there, reeking like a wino, and passed out holding her right shoe in her hand.

Every time the train stopped she smacked her head on the seat in front, and the rest of the time was being constantly shunted from my shoulder. The alcohol fumes were so overpowering that I eventually had to get up and stand by the window as my own alcohol-induced nausea returned.

When I got off, she was pressed against the window, holding her shoe aloft and fast asleep with her mouth open. I don't think I'll be touching alcohol again. I don't want to end up like that.

Friday 15 December

Someone gave us all Christmas cheer today by stealing the fucking copper wiring again. Cue a three-hour journey home. No Christmas cheer at all on our train this evening. Lumps of coal all round for the service.

Funnily enough, if we were coal-powered, at least nobody could stop us by stealing overhead lines, and we might actually be home on time for once.

Finally got my refund back for my ticket – funny how the train companies take the money instantly, but give it back slowly!

Monday 18 December

There are more drunken people on the train today and due to it being packed, I had to sit at a table with the worst of the pissheads.

"You're a pretty lady" he said to me about eight times. I love beer goggles.

He then started nudging the po-faced git next to him and tried to make him speak to me.

"You'd make a lovely couple, why don't you get together?" he slurred, about seven times.

I smiled politely and tried to make 'what's he like' eye contact with said miserable git.

Rather than just shrug it off, he looked at me like something the cat had just yakked up and said to drunken guy, "Please stop speaking to me, I do not want to get involved in this conversation. I have work to do."

Hey arsehole, you are no oil painting yourself, but have some fucking Christmas cheer!

Tuesday 19 December

Early morning train. My earphones on. A sixth sense tells me to look across at the man in the seat across the aisle. His lips are moving constantly.

I turn my music off and pull my earphones out. He is reading out loud to himself in a really creepy, whispery voice.

Nobody can actually hear what he is saying, we just know he is reading something out loud. This continues for the whole hour. I think I saw someone make the sign of the cross as they got off.

Wednesday 20 December

Christmas is nearly here!! Just two days to go until I have two weeks off! Whoop!

I decided to risk joining the queue of seasoned drinkers who congregate each day in the bar carriage and perhaps have a quick drink to celebrate another year nearly over.

But when I ask the price of a can of beer and they reply £7, I pretend I've forgotten my money and grab the nearest seat in the adjoining carriage. Even the most watered-down beer in London only costs £6. And at least it is usually cold.

Thursday 21 December

Really starting to wind down for the year

now, when a group of lads – they must be about thirteen or fourteen years old - pile on at the stop before mine with their mobile phones held out in their hands like some strange divining rods, and their crap music on loudspeaker.

It is amazing how bloody loud these phones are when you don't want them to be. Of course, they are playing some shitty rap/ RnB combo.

Some brave old man asks them to "Turn that racket down" and one of them – a pimply, pin-headed little shit says, "Oh fuck off, you stupid old wanker".

Ladies and gentlemen, I give you the workforce of the future.

Friday 22 December

Today is my last day of commuting for two whole weeks! The engineering works to ruin everybody's Christmas travel plans start tomorrow and I don't give a shit!! Suck it up, folks!! The trains actually ran on time both ways and I skipped up the hill to home, safe in the knowledge that I don't have to see another train for fourteen whole days.

Merry Christmas to you all.

Unless you run a railway franchise, that is.

If that is the case, I hope your oven breaks down on Christmas Day, you have been ridiculously ripped off for your turkey, and your plans are totally ruined for the entire festive period. But hey, sorry for any inconvenience!

Oh and a happy fucking new year too!